D1591709

FARM POWER

in the

MAKING OF AMERICA

By

Paul C. Johnson

Copyright 1978

Paul C. Johnson

Third Printing, 1981

Published by

Wallace-Homestead Book Co.
1912 Grand Avenue
Des Moines, Iowa 50305

Library of Congress Catalog Card Number 7793-178

ISBN: 0-87069-244-5

FRONT AND BACK COVERS: Steam threshing with bundle teams marked the most romantic period of farm history in the United States and Canada. The front cover illustration is used by courtesy of the Western Development Museum of Canada. BACK COVER is the front page of Prairie Farmer's centennial issue of 1941, celebrating the significance of mechanical power in agricultural history. Old farm magazine files were the chief source of information for this volume. Quite a number of farm publications are now more than 100 years old, during which time they played a leading role in improvement of farm efficiency and productivity.

Acknowledgments

OVER A PERIOD OF MANY YEARS many persons have had a hand in the making of this book. It is appropriate to acknowledge my debt to members of my family and neighbors who helped make my childhood on the farm interesting and who stimulated in me a lifelong love for the rural scene. Specifically, I thank the editors of *Prairie Farmer* and *Wallaces Farmer* for access to their files and collections of pictures. Many individuals have helped along the way: Margaret Connell, my secretary at *Prairie Farmer*, who always kept an eye out for historical material which later became invaluable to me; those who helped with information and materials, Lester Pulju, Orin Lofthus, Clarence Clausen, Gerhard Ellestad, Hulda Miller Schofield, Melferd Halling, LaVern J. Rippley, and the Western Development Museum of Canada; and not least those who appreciated my first two books of farm history so much that they egged me on to do another, Dr. and Mrs. Clem Granskou and Rex Hieronymous.

— Paul C. Johnson

Dedication

THIS BOOK IS DEDICATED to my wife Eveline who for all these years has been "good for everything that ails me." In a lifetime of editing and writing, I have known no one quite so sensitive to good writing, and no one so insistent on correctness in grammar and punctuation; skills that have become increasingly rare in this age of sloppy communication.

THE
PRAIRIE FARMER.
FARMERS WRITE FOR YOUR PAPER.

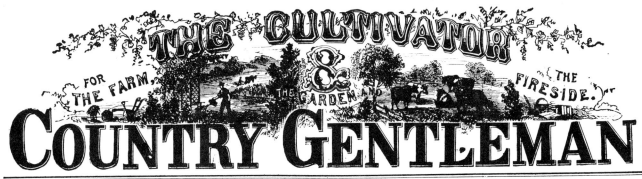

THE CULTIVATOR &
FOR THE FARM, THE GARDEN AND THE FIRESIDE.
COUNTRY GENTLEMAN

COMBINED PAPERS.
Forty-Ninth Year.

ALBANY, N. Y., JUNE 26, 1879.

COUNTRY GENTLEMAN,
VOL. XLIV---No. 1378.

ORANGE THE JUDD
FARMER.

Devoted to Farming ; to Live Stock of all Kinds ; to Dairying ; Markets ; to Horticulture in all its Branches ; to Housekeeping ; to the Young.

Vol. IV, No. 12.   308-316 Dearborn St.   CHICAGO, ILLINOIS, SEPTEMBER 22, 1888.   25 Cts. to Jan. 1, 1889.   One Dollar a Year.

WALLACES' FARMER
AND DAIRYMAN
A WEEKLY JOURNAL   FOR WESTERN FARMERS

VOL. XXII.   DES MOINES IOWA, FRIDAY, APRIL 16, 1897.   NO. 16.

PRINCIPAL SOURCE of both text and illustrations for this volume was a collection of bound volumes of old farm magazines, many of them more than 100 years old. Here are reproduced some of the ornate nameplates which were in themselves great examples of the engraver's art. Farm editors of the 1800s had an insatiable curiosity about mechanical things and were great boosters for the development of power to improve the efficiency of agriculture. The 1862 volume of Prairie Farmer, published in Chicago, is believed to have been the first to put a steam plow in its nameplate.

THE

AMERICAN AGRICULTURIST.

Agriculture is the most healthful, the most useful, and the most noble employment of Man.—*Washington.*

VOL. II.   NEW YORK, DECEMBER 15, 1843.   NO. XII.

A. B. ALLEN, Editor.   SAXTON & MILES, Publishers, 205 Broadway.

THE

FARMER'S GUIDE

A WEEKLY JOURNAL OF PROGRESSIVE AGRICULTURE.

Vol. XVI.—No. 19.   HUNTINGTON, INDIANA, MAY 7, 1904.   60 Cents per Year.

THE NEBRASKA FARMER.

Vol XXI.
No. 30.   LINCOLN, NEB., THURSDAY, JULY 22, 1897.   Whole No. 800

5

THIS MUSEUM REPRODUCTION of an American threshing scene before the Civil War shows a pre-Groundhog threshing machine powered by a simple one-horse treadmill or horsepower. The first practical use of a separate power unit on farms in this country was this simple device which converted animal muscle power to belt power needed for a number of farm machines. While wind and waterpower may have preceded the use of the treadmill on the ancient farms of the Middle East and Europe, the American farmer found the treadmill most useful for his purpose.

CONTENTS

FOREWORD

The two previously published books in this series, *Farm Animals in the Making of America (1976)* and *Farm Inventions in the Making of America (1976),* are a prelude to this volume on *Farm Power.* The muscle power of man and his trained beasts was, of course, the first conscious application of power to farming. For much of the known history of man, muscle was in fact about the only kind of applied power.

Mechanical inventions were for nearly 2000 years aimed at more efficient and intelligent use of muscle power. Experiments in the use of wind and flowing water to supplement muscle power go back to our earliest civilizations. However, it was not until around the middle of the 1800s that steam power was seriously considered as a substitute for muscle in an agriculture growing more sophisticated and more international in scope. Steam had its romantic half century but was never flexible enough, nor sufficiently applicable to the grass roots, to displace the ox, the mule, and the horse.

At the very close of the century the internal combustion engine and the electric motor began to attract the attention of farmers who had two overriding goals, to take up more of the abundant land in America, and to lift from farming, which required vast amounts of physical labor, the curse of drudgery. Thus began the massive shift from home grown feed and food to fossil fuels as the sources of energy for agriculture.

It took the energy crunch of the 1970s to call into question the heavy drain on petroleum and other fossil fuels, which are obviously non-renewable on this small planet. Words of warning, including my own, were raised as we built the energy requirements of modern mechanized agriculture to higher and higher peaks. The trend had the virtue of releasing more land for the growing of food for a sharply increasing world population. However, mechanized farming was bedeviled by growing surpluses and higher production costs which could not be entirely counteracted by its mounting efficiency.

In recent years economists as well as ecologists have wondered if we are nearing the point where the energy required to raise our crops will be greater than the energy the crops as food represent in the subsistence equation. Of course we can't equate in kilowatts or BTUs the food that fuels the human brain and sustains the human spirit with the oil that runs an internal combustion engine or heats a house! Or can we?

There is much here that confuses our food growing outlook and cries for honest research and broader perspectives as applied to the human condition.

Nevertheless, I do not think we should let the clouds on the immediate horizon detract from the successes that have been brought about by the intelligent, though sometimes too lavish, use of power (applied energy) to the goal of efficient farming. We are where we are — at the head of the world

food production class — largely because of our compulsive urge to use power other than muscle power to transform farming into a more productive and a more pleasant vocation.

In previous volumes I have written with enthusiasm about the empathy of the farmer and his animals, and about the inventiveness of the farmer in applying his brains and his ingenuity to the challenge of making an agricultural garden spot of the American continent.

The application of power to farming has to be the crowning achievement of the last century of agriculture. What changes will be required in the future to adjust these achievements to the fact of limited resources and a finite earth remain to be seen. The farmers who built the most productive agriculture the world has ever seen should be equal to this task also, with some help and understanding from the rest of us. As we move back to conservation and moderation in farming it is entirely possible that we may discover new qualities in rural life that have been obscured by our recent hectic pace.

Again I thank God for the privilege of living in both the age of the horse and buggy and the age of the tractor and automobile. It may not be my lot to see invention and technology brought under control, but at least I can make a start by revealing how the past shaped its legacy for us.

The time span covered by this book is roughly from the earliest uses of power (other than muscle power) in agriculture to around the year 1930, when the internal combustion engine went into its most modern phases, and electric power became commonplace on the farmstead. In other words, this is history, told from a personal point of view and largely from experience. The history before my time is taken mostly from the files of old farm magazines, of which I have a considerable collection. The published words of the farm editor (usually aiding and abetting the use of power on the farm, occasionally viewing it with skepticism) and the inventor-manufacturer plugging his products are raw history. Illustrations are largely from editorial colums, from farm publication advertisements, and from commerical pamphlets. Line drawings have the advantage that they tell the curious reader more about the construction of the machine than is possible with photographs.

Books on the history of the application of power to farming are not numerous, but there are a few good ones. These will be duly evaluated in the bibliographical comment. I am grateful to editors and authors for their help in permitting access to historical files and the "lifting" of old illustrations that often are of uncertain origin.

—PAUL C. JOHNSON

THIS DEMONSTRATION of steam power for agricultural purposes (plowing) is the subject of Plate XVII in the Yearbook of Agriculture. The important consideration was of course the replacement of men and horses to promote greater efficiency. It would appear here that this early steam tractor, the Redmond, could do the work of six men and twelve horses.

REDMOND'S STEAM PLOW.

9

THE WINDMILL was the trademark of the American family farm for well over 50 years. The neat barn with its fieldstone basement, one or more elaborate cupolas, and ramp for hauling in the hay, accompanied by windmill and silo, these all added up to good husbandry, prosperous farming, and congenial community life. The American system of farming is still unique among food producers of the world, dating back to the homestead law of 1862 which scattered farmsteads over open land capable of supporting a productive agriculture. Somehow this system, often criticised today as we go to larger units, laid the groundwork for our productivity and challenged the family farmer to find the best way of supporting his family and producing food for the world.

INTRODUCTION

When I speak of *Farm Power* in this book I am talking chiefly about mechanical power as applied to the operations of agriculture. We must not forget, however, that the muscles of man and his domesticated animals supplied nearly all of the power for farming for much of its history. Ironically, this muscle power was itself drawn in large part from a very basic agricultural process, namely photosynthesis, which utilizes solar energy in the growing plant to produce nutrients which enable man and beast to live and do their work.

When we switched from muscle power based on food and feed to concentrated fossil fuels running our engines we were merely going to the earth's storehouse of solar energy products. Fossil fuels are the residues of plants and animals of past ages which had been sus-

tained in large measure by solar energy working through photosynthesis. As we contemplate the possible exhaustion of those reserves, scientists are frantically trying to balance the energy equation by getting heat and electricity direct from the sun's rays. We seem to have come full circle.

As the old ditty goes, the ankle bone is connected to the leg bone and the leg bone is connected to the thigh bone and the thigh bone is connected to the hip bone!

We might have gone on indefinitely relying on muscle power except for the fact that some of the nourishment intended for human muscle was shunted off into man's steadily developing brain. Here things began to happen.

Man invented the wheel! At first the wheel was just a gimmick to reduce friction between the moving load and the surface under it. The strictly limited purpose was to move a load more handily. Power was still used almost entirely for draft purposes, that is to push or pull a load.

However, the wheel was destined for something greater than just to facilitate forward or backward movement of a load. It became the principal means of doing all kinds of work when power was applied to the wheel itself. If the wheel was to become the driver rather than the facilitator, power had to be applied in a circular or spinning motion instead of in a straight pull or push. This manuever was not too difficult for a person with brains. He could apply his muscle in a circular motion by cranking instead of pushing.

To get this spinning motion from an animal, or flowing water or wind, was quite another matter. So the inventors applied themselves to what we later came to call "belt" power.

The first power machines fell into this category. They started by putting muscle power to turning a wheel, and went on to harness in this way other sources of power, such as wind, water, steam, internal combustion, electricity.

Today muscle power in agriculture has become almost obsolete. The farmer, like the desk worker, has to get his exercise in the recreational arena. He is plagued by overweight even as the city worker. The food that used to be burned up in the creation of muscle power, now finds its way to his rear where its only use is to supplement the foam rubber on the tractor seat.

There is scant consolation in the fact that the brain also requires an input of energy, as does a high state of worry about the increasing complexity of farming.

Muscle power did not yield the field to mechanical power without something of a battle. Availability of slave labor slowed the change for many centuries. So also did the age old concepts of "honest labor" and "the sweat of the brow" as evidences of economic worth and even moral status. Our much discussed Protestant ethic had in it a considerable content of faithful labor, mostly physical.

While rural culture idealized honest labor, it also chafed under its yoke. Farmers have always had to struggle to keep green their sense of vocation. They found it easy to speak of farming as drudgery. Lifting this drudgery from their shoulders was a principal reason for both invention and education. The latter moved the younger generation into less oppressive (they thought) professions. The former made farming more endurable.

This is not to say that many farmers did not indeed have a sense of pride in their vocation. They loved their land and their livestock. The work done by a stout ox or a faithful horse was idealized along with the work done by man himself.

Displacing the ox, the horse and the mule was met with some resentment and a good deal of opposition. The age of steam as applied to farming (roughly defined as 1850 to 1900) had very little effect on the use of horses for both farming and transportation. Steam was too cumbersome and too expensive for most farmers. It took over mostly the heaviest belt work such as threshing. The arrival of the gas tractor at the turn of the century brought the real confrontation between horse power and mechanical power. Even so, horses were dominant in farming the first quarter of the 1900s and did not really lose the battle to the internal combustion engine until the middle thirties.

It was a colorful battle, because horse enthusiasts were often colorful people. Horses were more than a source of power. Like people, they were flesh and blood and personality, and contributed uncertainty and excitement.

The tractor advocates had efficiency on their side, efficiency based in part on ridiculously low fuel cost. It is hard to believe now that gasoline could be bought for ten cents a gallon, and kerosene and other cruder distillates for even less. Counter arguments were mustered in impressive array: tractors were taking the romance and spiritual rewards out of farming; they were ruining the land; they were undermining the nation's morals; they required purchased fuel rather than home grown feed.

The outcome was never in doubt, but the battle was spirited while it lasted.

Some of the better arguments for the horse arrived on the scene much later. There can be very little doubt that the 60 million acres of good farm land released when farmers turned from raising their own energy in the form of horsefeed to buying it from the tankwagon had a great deal to do with the price-depressing surpluses of recent decades. No thought was given to the possibility of petroleum supplies becoming more expensive or being exhausted completely. In the horse and buggy period it was often pointed out that the exhaust of a mule or a horse is good for the land while the exhaust of the tractor is not. However, practically nobody thought that the exhaust of the internal combustion engine might actually do harm to the environment.

In the volume on *Farm Inventions* I had a good deal to say about the mechanical ingenuity of the American farmer and his near cousins, the country blacksmith and the neighborhood handyman. The early development of farm implements and farmstead labor savers merely whetted their appetites for the development of farm power. The blacksmith shop was readily converted into a back street machine shop or garage. The "empathy between horse and man" which I described with such feeling in *Farm Animals* was not characteristic of all rural people. This empathy was something special which enriched the lives of the horsey set and dedicated livestock breeders.

Most farmers were just interested in getting the work done. They were not reluctant to give up horses. Although the balky engine was not unlike the balky horse in end result, the engine offered a challenge which appealed to many. It would be hard to say whether the livestock elite were better people than the mechanically gifted farmers, or more numerous. In any event mechanical ingenuity has probably done

more for the development of productive farming than the art of animal husbandry.

Many will disagree violently with the above statement, but the figures are there to argue in favor of mechanization. This evidence will grow even stronger as an overpopulated world turns more agricultural produce into "people food" and less into animal feed.

Turning push-pull muscle power into wheel power took a long time — centuries in fact. One of the earliest and crudest devices was to fasten wooden buckets to the rim of a tall wooden wheel to lift water out of a stream for irrigation. Such machines are still in use in many parts of the world. More modern metal versions are the cistern pumps still to be found in antiques shops which hook buckets on a belt activated by two wheels and a crank.

The Dutch type windmill was invented more or less simultaneously in several parts of the world. It was refined considerably in the American windmill which dotted every rural scene from around 1860 on. Today the eyes of energy conscious inventors are once more on this machine, and for the first time we may get around to applying modern engineering to harnessing the power of the wind.

Harnessing power, whether muscle power or the forces of nature, took a lot of inventing. The treadmill required a belt to turn a wheel. The sweep power which also utilized horses primarily had to wait for a strong, metal, bevel gear that would change the plane in which power was delivered. Crude gears made of wooden pegs would no longer suffice. The crank and connecting rod were essential to both steam and internal combustion engines. They were not all that different from muscle power in that push-pull was converted into spin. The same prin-

ciple was followed when magnetic push-pull was converted to spin by means of the electric motor.

In most, but not all, sources of power, fuel is a limiting factor which has to be dealt with. Fuels have to be grown or mined before they can be burned to produce energy to produce power to do work. Fuels are usually divided into two classes, the renewable and the non-renewable. Usually neither comes cheap, and the latter always faces the possibility of reserves becoming exhausted. Even so-called free power is never really free. Solar energy, the wind, and the force of gravity which activates the waterfall still have to be harnessed, and harnessing is often very expensive.

This volume will make no effort to treat all sources of energy — only those which had an important impact on farming up to the 1930s. We will take a look at the horsepower (treadmill and sweep) which merely put farm animals to work in a different way. Wind and water power will come in for attention, especially the former which was well adapted to the individual farm. The steam engine with all its romance has been written about extensively, but it belongs right in the center of the farm picture. The gas tractor and how it grew will get the most attention here because its invention and development, from the turn of the century until it reached the age of sophistication in the 1930s, has not been widely described.

THE HORSE was the backbone of power for agriculture for so many generations that the conversion to the tractor cost a good deal of effort and much trauma. One of the problems was adapting the tractor to horse-drawn equipment. Manufacturers came up with tractors that could be driven with reins. The idea didn't last long but it did have its place in the transition.

BELOW IS SHOWN the sweep horse-power in what was probably its most advanced state of development. The power was transmitted to the threshing machine by a tumbling rod. This one dates from around 1890. It utilized six teams (12 horses). The largest ever built was probably for seven teams. As threshing machines grew larger, most farmers turned to steam power, but some distrusted steam and insisted on using horses. Development of the powerful sweep horse-powers came later than the treadmills because they required a set of bevel gears to transmit the circular motion from horizontal to vertical.

HORSEPOWERS

Power for pioneering

The progress of agriculture through the centuries has been dependent to a large degree on the invention of machines to improve the effectiveness of the farmer and his draft animals. Farming has always, as is the case today, consumed large amounts of power — to break up the soil, to hold down weeds, to handle crops in their many stages, and to process them into usable forms. At one time, most of these operations were the province of the farmer himself. He had good reason for wanting to make his work more fruitful and his life more bearable.

This was largely accomplished

The Dingee Woodbury Power.

by applying available power — at first the muscle power of man and beast — to the implement which did the work, whether plowing or seeding, harvesting, shredding or grinding. As sources of power other than muscle power were harnessed, it became more desirable to have power separate from the operating machines, portable if possible, flexible so that the same power unit might be used for several purposes.

Here again, as with most farm inventions, the ideas and the first crude models were the products of the farm and country blacksmith shop. Farmers sensed what was needed and set to work to invent and build something to do the job. It was pointed out in a previous volume, *Farm Inventions in the Making of America*, that blacksmith craftsmen such as Jerome I. Case, John Deere and Cyrus McCormick all started this way and later became the founders of the great machinery empires that bore their names. While we are familiar with only a few such names, there were actually hundreds of "jackleg" inventors who worked first at the job of building the farm machines and then hitching up the power to make them go.

Harnessing wind and water for agricultural tasks was attempted by Persians, Greeks, Romans and other early civilizations. The Anglo-Saxons seem to have been more persistent in their efforts to convert the push-pull power of the ox, horse and mule into the rotating or belt power needed for the increasingly complicated machines of farming.

Thus were born the treadmill and the sweep horsepower. These did not tap a new source of power, as was the case later with the steam engine, internal combustion engine or electric motor. They utilized the traditional animal power but set the power unit up

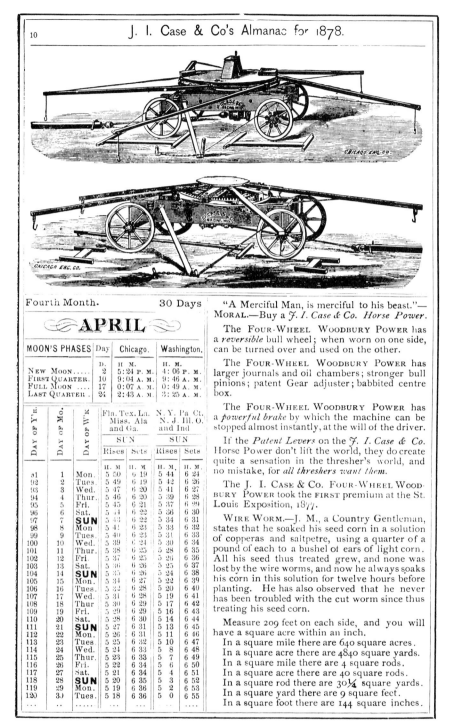

THIS ADVERTISEMENT from the J. I. Case Almanac of 1878 will give the reader a better idea of the sweep power and a chance to read what the manufacturer had to say about it. Case was the world's largest builder of threshing machines. He sold horsepowers to fit his machines until the turn of the century, long after he had developed serviceable steam engines. Case bought patents from other companies — in this case Woodbury — and sold machines under his own brand name.

Dog Power.—Fig. 77.

THE above cut represents a machine or power to be propelled by a dog, sheep, or other small animal, for the purpose of churning, working a washing-machine, turning a grind stone, or working small mills of any kind. It is a very simple and complete apparatus, and would be found profitable on many farms, or in many other situations. It was invented by PALMER & FROST, of Poughkeepsie, N. Y., and is sold at $15.

THE EARLIEST HORSEPOWERS were in fact dog-powers, rather crudely built to do smaller farmstead tasks such as churning butter, operating washing machines, or pumping water. In fact, goats, sheep and even children were utilized to work the treads, as well as dogs and cattle. The circular tread wheel was shown in a Prairie Farmer of the year 1846. The other two are from Cultivator magazines of 1847 and 1869. Dogs are said to have enjoyed the work and required no confinement or urging.

as a separate unit. The powers changed push-pull into a rotating motion which was then transmitted to the operating machine either by belt, linkchain, or a tumbling rod.

The treadmill utilized the weight and energy of the animal by forcing it to walk uphill on a moving floor which activated the drums around which this endless floor-belt was wrapped. There were many variations of this belt-on-drum principle, depending on the type of animal used and the amount of power that was generated. Small powers run by dogs or goats were sometimes in the form of a wheel. Large powers, using as many as three horses abreast, were more massive in construction. They were used to furnish power for big machines such as threshers, timber saws, ensilage cutters, and the like.

Even a three-horse treadmill did not deliver power enough to handle the large capacity threshers that were coming into use during the last quarter of the 1800s. So sweep powers were invented. Also called lever powers, they had several poles radiating out from a powerfully built hub. To the outer end of these poles were hitched teams of horses or other draft animals that walked in a circle.

DOG POWER FOR CHURNING.

EDS. COUNTRY GENTLEMAN—Can you give a description of the best plan for churning by dog power?
Mt. Vernon, O.   I. M. M.

The annexed engraving (fig. 1) exhibits the dog power for churning very clearly. It can be obtained at all large

Fig. 1.
Agricultural Warehouses at the east—price $22.

The biggest sweep horsepowers used as many as six teams or twelve horses, all applying their energy to turning the giant wheel in a circle.

The big sweep powers were not feasible until cast iron bevel gears could be manufactured to transmit the leverage of the multiple teams into usable power. It was also necessary to change the axis from vertical to horizontal so that power might be carried by heavy tumbling rods to the threshers or other machines. The larger and increasingly sophisticated threshing machines needed both power and speed, which meant that the slow measured turn of the sweep had to be multiplied greatly by means of the gear ratio and pulley systems.

As the teams moved in a circle, the horses had to step over the housing of the spinning tumbling rod at each round and move at a steady pace. It was no job for a fractious animal. The operator of the teams sat or stood in the middle over the axle and gear housing and cracked his whip to keep up this steady motion. Since the contraption added its grinding and creaking noise to that of the thresher, a good signal system between the driver and the threshing machine operator was certainly needed.

Sweep powers ranged in size and complexity from a simple gear assembly with one or two spokes, staked down to hold it in position, to a well-constructed and nicely painted gear box on four stout wheels, fitted with removable sweeps that could be stacked on the machine for moving from job to job.

Both the treadmill and the sweep power started out as relatively crude contraptions of timber, held together by roughly forged straps, bolts and cleviess. In the 60-year period when the

THE ABOVE contraption, shown in an 1853 Prairie Farmer, shows a horsepower of the treadmill type used to saw wood. The illustration at left, from an 1862 Prairie Farmer, is of an overhead sweep power with surprisingly advanced gearing. Both churn and power in the lower illustration were sold by the Cherry Company of Chicago which specialized in dairy equipment. There is something of poetic justice in putting the bull to work churning the butter from the herd.

❧ **Improved**
❧ **United**
❧ **States**
❧ **Cream**
❧ **Separator.**

* * *

17

HORACE L. EMERY'S PATENT
Endless Railway Horse-Power,
MANUFACTURED BY
H. L. EMERY & SONS,
PROPRIETORS OF THE
ALBANY AGRICULTURAL WORKS,
ALBANY, N. Y.

The invention of this Horse-Power, in 1848-9, was the result of a long and successful mechanical experience and observation, since which it has acquired the widest introduction, reputation, sale and use, and for twenty-five years has continued without a superior or equal, and almost without a rival, for all purposes of the Farm, Plantation or Workshop requiring the Utilization of Animal Power.

Its manufacturers have been awarded more premiums, medals, diplomas and honors for superiority at public fairs and trials throughout the country than have been awarded to all other kinds combined.

They are more Efficient, Compact, Portable, Simple, Durable, Adjustable, Changeable, Adaptable, Safer, Lighter, Stronger and Cheaper than any other Railway Power extant, and have long since been the acknowledged standard power by the users, dealers and manufacturers of Railway Powers, and the agricultural public generally.

Among the numerous advantages are greater ease of operation, and efficiency, with less labor for the animals working them; their superior workmanship, and kinds of materials used in their construction, all the working parts being made of Malleable Iron and Steel, instead of grey Cast Iron and Wrought Iron, which are universally used by all other manufacturers. Their frame work is of best Ash Timber, instead of cheaper and less durable woods.

The greater diameters of all their gears and pinion wheels, and forked reels, and longer and larger journals and bearings, give them fully quadruple the amount of contact and wearing surfaces, and strength and durability. The teeth of all the gears are cycloidal in form, which produces perfectly equable motion, with the least friction and wear, and greatest strength.

Its series of couplings upon the ends of both its main shafts, as also all its series of gears and pulleys, are outside of the frame work, where they are instantly accessible for transposition, lubrication and care, instead of being unchangeable, and within and beneath the moving platform, exposed to the droppings of the animals, and inaccessible for cleaning, lubrication or adjustment.

They are furnished with several gears and pulleys of different diameters, which can be instantly transposed to produce all the different speeds and forces desired for driving different machines without changing the labor of the animals. All the bearings are lined with Babbett metal. The main shafts are mounted on movable bearings, for the ready adjustment of the tension and running of the endless platform, by which friction, wear and loss of power are avoided, and Efficiency and Durability always ensured, however old and great their amount of use and wear.

It is the cheapest of all kinds in use, when it is considered that the first cost for construction and materials exceeds by nearly fifty per cent. that of others, without their advantages, and the prices for which are the same, or within two and a half to five per cent. of the prices asked for the better power.

LEVER HORSE-POWERS.

We also manufacture the most approved Lever Powers, with Double Bull Pinions, and Balanced Gearing with Tumbling Shafts, Housed Couplings and Jack—the latter containing a series of gears and pulleys, with pawl and ratchet couplings, for producing by transposition the several degrees of force and motion required.

They have double braced levers, also entire cast iron bed plate, containing all the Babbetted bearings and shafting, and mounted on a substantial oak timber bed or ground frame.

They are adapted for one, two, four, six and eight horses, for Threshing, Ginning, Sawing and Milling purposes.

Threshers with Cleaners,

Also with SEPARATORS, and without either, for Horse, Steam and Water Power, and for all kinds of Grain, Rice, Grass and Garden Seeds, and for all countries.

They, like the Horse-Powers, are thoroughly made, and of superior materials, and are sold at even prices with all the leading and competing machines, which last lack many of the most essential advantages belonging to our own, and whose cost for construction and materials range far less.

For further and full particulars, descriptions, illustrations, prices and terms of sale and warranty, consult our Catalogue for 1873-4, furnished gratis to all addresses on receipt of a two-cent stamp.

Address, with care, **H. L. EMERY & SONS,**
PROPRIETORS OF THE
Albany Agricultural Works,
ALBANY, N. Y.

HORACE L. EMERY,
H. HERBERT EMERY,
CHAS. FRED. EMERY.

TAKE THE TIME to read this advertisement from the Country Gentleman and Cultivator of 1873, and you will learn a good bit about the machinery of that day. Emery and Sons were among the largest eastern manufacturers of threshing machines and other farm machinery.

---

powers were in common use they changed considerably. After the Civil War most farm machinery companies built or at least marketed their own powers. In order to sell their machines they had to be able to recommend a power unit to go with them. At the turn of the century, 30 years after steam had come into use and just at the dawn of the gasoline age, horsepowers were still being sold. Case offered one with his separators well into the 1890s, long after he had developed steam engines to go with his threshing machine.

Many farmers were suspicious of steam, citing fear of explosions, plus the usual arguments for sticking with tried and true horses.

Very little was printed in the farm magazines of the time about the troubles with horsepowers which must have been many and annoying. In spite of crude governors and brakes, driving speeds must have fluctuated in ways that interfered with the efficiency of the machine being powered. Training horses, mules, oxen, cows, bulls, goats and dogs to furnish steady and reliable power must have been a headache. The slatted belts of the treadmills must have been hard on horses' feet.

The sweep powers employing several teams had fulltime drivers who kept the teams in proper motion. Horses on the treadmill were held in position by traces and straps while they trudged their way up the never ending incline. Theoretically it was impossible for the animal to stop, but we can be sure it happened frequently. There were undoubtedly good treadmill animals and bad ones.

As a small boy on the farm around the year 1910, the author observed the frustrations of the last of the horsepowers, used on our farm to pump water whenever the windmill failed. The small power had two sweeps linked to a pumpjack by a tumbling rod. A reliable old horse was hitched to one sweep and tied with a halter rope to another ahead of him. He was giddapped into motion, but the problem was to keep him going untended. A young boy usually had to be stationed nearby to holler giddap frequently and to shy pebbles at the horse's rear. The progress was very slow or much too fast, depending on the mood of the horse, the peskiness of the flies, or the alertness of the boy sitting nearby.

As steam began to gain headway as a source of power for threshers and other power hungry farm machines, there began to appear in the farm magazines articles in the defense of horsepowers which had been more or less taken for granted. What is more interesting, we get some glimpses of the horse's point of view with respect to this primitive machine that bears his name.

L. A. Brown of Knox County, Illinois, writes in *Country Gentleman* of 1891:

"Recent articles on horse tread-powers remind me of the first that I ever saw — I think in 1843. It was noised about in the neighborhood that a Captain (so and so) had gone after a one-horse threshing machine, and would thresh all the grain in the country. In due time it was announced that he would be at our house to thresh our grain on a certain day. I was 12 years old and looked forward to the coming of the thresher as to a circus. When the day arrived and the captain, with a great flourish, drove the thresher up to the barn, it looked to me nearly as grand as a four-horse coach. Giving us to understand that what he didn't know about threshing and handling horses was not worth knowing, the captain soon had the machine set and 50 sheaves

A. W. GRAY'S SONS of Middletown Springs, Vermont, had a full line of treadmills including one that used three horses side by side. The ad is from Country Gentleman of 1878.

Gray & Son's Three-Horse Tread Power.

MACHINES FOR THRESHING AND CLEANING GRAIN,
ALSO
MACHINES FOR SAWING WOOD,
With Circular and Cross-Cut Drag Saws,
PATENTED, MANUFACTURED AND SOLD BY
A. W. GRAY'S SONS, Middletown Springs, Vermont.

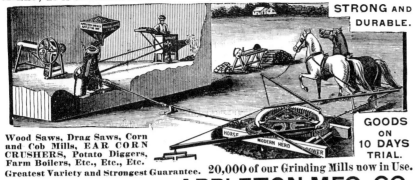

ordered for the first 'flooring'. A large bony horse was brought to the foot of the power; his eyes showed that he did not like to go up there, but with threats and loud words he was got up — a strong man checking him from going over the power. The tugs hooked so he could not go out forward, the bale-strap fastened to prevent backing out, a chain under his belly so he could not lie down — and the horse was ready. One man was stationed with a hand-rake to rake the straw from the grain, one with a fork to carry the straw back, and I was appointed to cut bands. When all was ready, the captain loosened the brake and the horse started. I had a band-cut sheaf on the table, the captain caught it; I cut another band and had the sheaf in its place; then I looked to see the captain sift it into the machine. It seemed wonderful; his motions were something like a conceited professor playing a pipe organ. All at once the old horse began to pull back and tried to lie down — then you should have heard the captain! Soon the horse began to walk again and the 50 sheaves were threshed. Fifty more were ordered down, then we should change horses. All was soon ready and a fresh horse was started and 50 sheaves were threshed, but the 'power' was not ready to stop; he kept surging forward and backward after the machine stopped."

So much for the captain and his unwilling horses, but this was not the whole picture.

A more balanced evaluation of the horsepower, also published in *Country Gentleman* in the year 1891, was submitted by A. J. Cook of Michigan Agricultural College. By that time the powers were largely factory made and were giving the steam engines a run for their money. Here is Cook's

20

account: "I have now used the tread-power for some years on my farm, and I like it very much. I examined the question very fully before I bought, and decided that the tread was greatly superior to the sweep-power from its greater convenience and efficiency, and to the steam engine, from convenience and safety. Several years of actual trial confirm my early judgment in every respect.

"The tread-power is about twice as effective with the same number of horses as is the sweep-power. It is always — or may be — right in the barn, and so we are out of the rain. It needs no person to drive the horses, as with this power the horses *must* go. We can put the tread-power in a very small space, and in almost any position with reference to our cutter, our grindstone, etc., and so can arrange to have everything done in the most convenient manner. In my own case I could not use either steam or sweep-power in filling my silos at any advantage. Either would prevent drawing stalks close beside the cutter. For this alone I should much prefer the tread-power.

"I have known several fires from engines and more than one explosion; though not very likely, the very terror of such occurrences makes me happier with some other apparatus. As I have said, we can often arrange far more conveniently with a tread-power than with an engine. Again, the cost of an engine is no small objection. The objection that the tread is hard on horses is more sentiment than fact. I do not hesitate at all to put my horses or colts in this machine. They seem not to mind it at all, and in winter are as well, if not better, for doing this work. It does not seem hard, and affords excellent exercise.

"My power — the Morton — has two governors, either one of

which will stop the extra motion, even if the belt runs off while in full motion, as we have actually proved by trial. These governors are so simple and strong that one does not see how they can break. Certainly the two would never break at the same time; so we may feel that this power is entirely safe.

"A very great recommendation for my tread-power rests in the fact that I can hitch on to it and move it from barn to barn, or barn to woodlot, as quickly and easily as on a wagon. This is no mean recommendation. The cost — something over $100 — is considerable, but as it will last indefinitely we are the more ready to pay this sum without complaint. My power will run a No. 14 cutter, so as to take green stalks for the silo as fast as anyone can get them to the feeder; this, when we cut an inch long. If we cut shorter than this, we cannot run quite so fast, but I see no advantage in cutting any shorter. As yet I have never regretted the purchase of this admirable power."

THE FINAL CHAPTER of the horse-powers was written in the 1890s, although some were in use well into the 1900s. Above is one of the last and most sophisticated Appleton tread-powers. On the opposite page are three of the small sweeps which continued in use for shelling corn, grinding feed, pumping water, and operating dairy equipment well into the new century. A one-horse sweep was used on the Minnesota farm where the author was a boy, as late as 1912 to pump water when the windmill failed.

THIS IS THE ACTUAL photograph taken about 1902 of a large Dutch type windmill built on a hilltop in Dakota County, Minnesota, between 1892 and 1894. It was built from locally hewn and sawed timber by a miller-carpenter named Magnus Miller, newly arrived from southern Sweden where such mills were common. For ten or twelve years Miller ground grain for nearby farmers, turning out as many as 800 sacks in a long day and night run when the wind was right. Eventually he gave up trying to deal with the uncertain Minnesota winds and procured a second hand Flour City tractor, an old "one-lunger" that was almost as hard to handle as the clumsy vanes of the windmill. The wheel span was over 60 feet. The pole at the back indicates that this was a cone type mill which was turned into the wind by means of a huge lever at the back. Speed was controlled in part by brakes and also by the amount of sail roped to the giant wooden vanes. It was a dangerous piece of machinery, prone to running away in a sudden windstorm.

Watermills and windmills deserve treatment in the same chapter even though the latter were much more widely utilized as a source of power on individual farms. The watermill (more often called the waterwheel) was essentially a community resource. The mill powered by water became the focal point of grist-milling as a community service, and was occasionally used also to saw timber or even thresh grain.

The windmill, on the other hand, was better adapted to small farm use. Millions were manufactured and put to work by the year 1900 in America alone.

Both watermill and windmill used a natural and mostly renewable force as a source of power. Running water and moving air were there to be used from the beginning, challenging the inventiveness of man, both as means of transportation and as forces to be harnessed to do work.

Watermills and windmills had very early origins. Persians are believed to have developed the first contraptions before the time of Christ. It is said that the Greeks adapted the ideas from the Persians, and the Romans from the Greeks. The first watermills were used to lift irrigation water out of streams and ditches by means of buckets fastened to the spokes of the wheel. While these wheels were originally turned by human or animal power, it was an easy step to widen the spokes into paddles and let the force of the stream lift the buckets that carried the water upward.

Even though the Romans were great inventors, they were slow to develop water power for agricultural uses. It has been suggested that progress was hampered by a superstitious reluctance to harness the work of gods for agriculture which was closely tied to divine intervention in all its aspects. More likely the abundance of slave and peasant labor in farming reduced the incentive to mechanize.

The Romans are credited with bringing watermills to Britain where streams were abundant. Nearly every manor in the feudal period had its own water-powered grist mill. This system was transplanted to colonial America and established in the East where grist mills became centers of community activity.

Watermills will be passed over lightly here because sites were available only in tidal areas or in hilly country. Even there the sites were sought out by pioneer business entrepreneurs rather than farmers because of the extra capi-

THE OVERSHOT WATERMILL
shown above was the type used mostly in water-driven grist mills scattered over the eastern sections of the United States in pioneer times. The detail at left is of an undershot wheel equipped with little buckets on the paddles to lift water out of a ditch.

tal needed to build dams and mills. These sites often became centers of local commerce, as well as the social centers where churches and schools were erected. The mill pond was the place for ice cutting, ice skating, and even for winter horse racing.

The grist or flour mill site was where farmers assembled with loads of grain to be ground, and where larger commercial mills were later erected. These became markets where grain was bought from farmers, and flour was milled, packed in sacks or barrels and shipped all over the country, even abroad.

Few pioneer farmers found themselves with usable sites on which to develop waterpower for farm tasks. However, those who did, and who also had the enterprise to utilize them, made a considerable contribution to early development of farm power.

For a watermill you needed a flowing stream which had a rather steep fall (or head) and was reliable in all seasons. Wheels, as well as sluices to direct the water against the blades of the wheels, were made of wood, held together by straps and elbows from the local blacksmith shops. An overshot wheel was most often used, especially where water could be diverted from a fast stream well above the mill site and directed against the vanes or buckets of a large wheel. The weight of the water caused it to turn briskly.

A breast-shot wheel was sunk almost to its axle in a flowing stream and got its impetus from the large volume of water passing under it. There were also undershot wheels, more often used in harnessing trapped tides, where a limited stream of water was directed under a wheel to make it turn.

One of the problems of the waterwheel used to power a grist mill was that the millstones did their work on a horizontal plane, requiring that the power furnished by the wheel be converted from the horizontal axis of the wheel to a vertical shaft which turned the millstones. The conversion required a large beveled gear — if made of iron — or a series of wooden pegs engaging the wooden teeth of a crude horizontal gear. Sometimes the gears were of concrete with imbedded wooden teeth.

The building and maintenance of wooden gears of sufficient strength to turn large millstones was a formidable task. Consequently, there also developed many ingenious devices for delivering the stream of water into a horizontal wheel with wooden vanes set on a slant, or metal vanes curved very much as the marine propellors of today.

The crude, lumbering waterwheels began to be replaced in the late 1800s by hydraulic rams for lifting water, and turbines which called for more intricate castings and better bearings than the large wheels. The former utilized the weight of a large volume of water from a stream to force a much smaller volume to greater heights than the original stream. The latter enclosed a much smaller waterwheel in a metal housing and introduced the water through a pipe, essentially as we do in steam and water turbines today.

Small turbines and rams were developed for farm use, but they had little acceptance because of limited access to usable streams and the cost of building dams. This was not for the small farmer.

THE CULTIVATOR
AND
Country Gentleman
Albany, August 21, 1879.

Improved Farm Machinery---XIII.

Water Power.

Among important improvements which have been largely introduced of late years is the turbine water-wheel. The large wooden overshot wheels have to hold and carry all the water while its force is acting. Turbine wheels do not hold the water, but merely act from its pressure in the flume above. Hence one of quite small size, receiving all the force of a high column of water, may impart great force to machinery. Turbine wheels are horizontal, and the water acts at once on the whole circumference. Being under water, they do not freeze. They are not stopped by the back water of a flood.

The annexed cut (fig. 1) represents the tur-

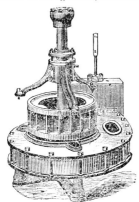

Fig. 1.---*Carley's Turbine Wheel.*

bine wheel made by the Cortland Foundry and Machine Company, Cortland, N. Y., and known as Carley's turbine. The orifice is shown, through which the water is admitted to the whole circumference of the wheel. Fig. 2 shows the wheel lifted out of the case, and the form and the arrangement of the buckets, which are made of steel or wrought iron, cast into the rims

Fig. 3.---*Leffel's Turbine Wheel.*

required to sustain the heavy weight of water in the flume above.

Among the largest turbine wheels which have ever been made are those manufactured by Jas. Leffel & Co. of Springfield, Ohio, the wheel proper being 8 feet in diameter, with a head over 10 feet. Higher heads usually require less size of wheel. In one instance they made an exceedingly strong 19-inch wheel, for 300 feet head, and with 80-horse power. One of the most powerful wheels which they have in operation is a 35-inch wheel, under a 64-feet head, giving 400-horse power. It was made in the best, strongest and most substantial manner, mostly of steel and bronze, and the shaft was of solid forged steel. They have put four wheels in one mill, each 7 feet in diameter, each of which possesses, when run at full capacity, 460-horse power. We mention these instances to show the great power possessed by turbine wheels.

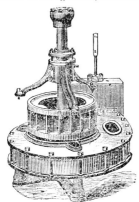

Fig. 2.---*Wheel Lifted Out of Case.*

of the wheel, imparting to it the great strength

THESE COLUMNS from an 1879 issue of The Cultivator and Country Gentleman reveal early attempts to adapt waterpower for use on the small farm. The waterpowered grist mill was usually not an individual farm enterprise but a community service project of a private entrepreneur. For the smaller farm the hydraulic ram for lifting water uphill was perfected as early as 1870, and efforts were made to build small cast-iron turbines to utilize waterpower. Because of costs and a lack of suitable waterpower sites, these attempts to build a farm-size turbine did not prosper. Farmers of the 1800s turned to wind as their cheapest and most flexible source of power for farm tasks.

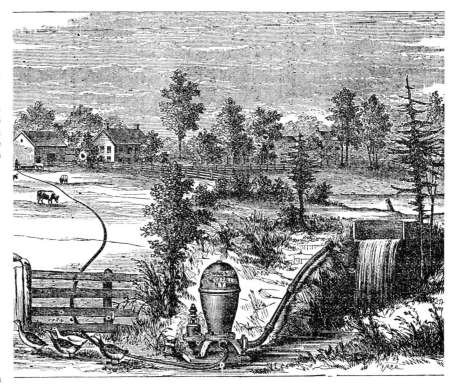

Today as we search frantically for cheaper renewable sources of energy, the windmill is coming under closer scrutiny. It looks as if, at long last, the capture of wind power will get the benefit of our best engineering and technology in an effort to utilize a natural force which is all around us "going to waste." It would seem that with our advances in eliminating friction, our study of aerodynamics through the use of wind tunnels, and our modern means of storing power, we should be able to do something pretty spectacular with the ancient and honorable windmill.

Wind power has already proved its adaptability to the needs of the farm. It can be put to work on a smaller scale and with lower capital investment than its partner, water power. On the other hand, it has labored under the disadvantage of being intermittent and unreliable in most parts of the world. For instance, its use has almost ceased in the eastern and midwestern sections of America, where winds are variable as to both direction and force. At the same time, the small windmill has continued in use by the millions out in the western ranch country where winds blow steadily day and night and where pumped wells have replaced the waterholes of pioneer times.

The simple windmill in use today calls for a minimum of engineering. It is a metal wheel on a metal tower with slanting or curv-

THE FIRST FARM windmills such as the one at left were simple devices of wood, usually hitched directly to a pump rod by means of a crank. Soon after 1850 windmills developed rapidly into much more sophisticated machines such as the one above. There were eight-, ten- and twelve-foot wheels supported on wooden frames from 20 to 40 feet in height. The slats were usually of wood although the wheel frames were of metal. Later both the wheels and towers were made of metal, galvanized to relieve the farmer of an odious painting job.

26

ed spokes. The wheel is swung into a position facing the wind by a vane or rudder which is usually manipulated by hand to stop, start or give limited control over the speed. A simple gearbox running in oil transmits circular into up-and-down motion which operates a piston pump underground. This is the basic windmill which we encounter by the thousands in western ranch country but which has become increasingly rare in the Midwest, South and East.

Looking at the windmill historically we find, somewhat to our surprise, that a lot more engineering and craftsmanship — one might even say sheer genius — went into its construction during the Middle Ages than is true today. When America decided that all the windmill was good for was to pump water, our engineers turned their attention to other means of capturing and creating power. During the period when the automobile has been developed into a precision machine, when diesel power has taken over much of our farming and practically all of our rail transportation, and the airplane (which must be some kind of a shirt-tail relation of the windmill) has risen to great heights of engineering, the windmill has remained relatively unchanged. In fact, for farm use, we had much more complex and better engineered windmills in the last quarter of the 1800s than we have today.

That isn't to say that the windmill has been abandoned. Pumping water from wells has long been an important need on the farm. Many small manufacturers in the industrial Midwest, and especially at Batavia, Illinois, worked up an enormous business in farm windmills. Six and a half million windmills were built in the United States between 1880 and 1930. There are only a few companies left of the hundred or more that

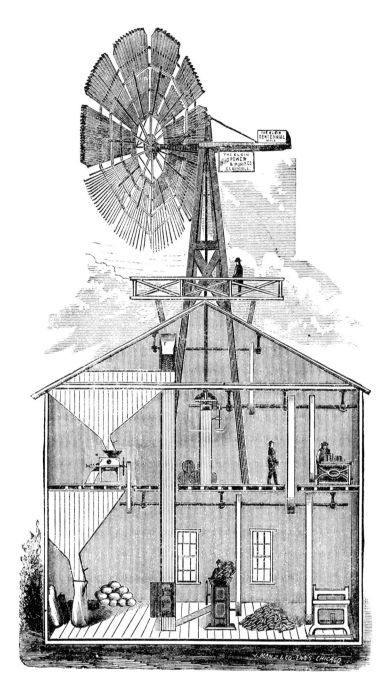

were once in the business, but these are doing quite well. This past year it is estimated that 4,000 windmills were sold in the United States. It remains to be seen whether the current companies will branch out to build more sophisticated mills as we return to wind power, or whether the big automotive and farm machinery firms will recognize its bright future.

BUILDING windmills on top of barns and other service buildings was a common practice. It saved tower materials and also facilitated the hookup to various machines which needed power.

TURBINE WIND MILL.
CALIFORNIA'S FAVORITE
And the Favorite of every one who has seen or used it.

The Turbine is all under cover, completely protected from the weather, and will last a lifetime for

Pumping Water, Grinding Feed, Sawing Wood, Etc

COUNTRY GENTLEMAN in the 1880s presented proudly this engraving of the elaborate Hopkins barn near Providence, Rhode Island. It was complete with an Eclypse windmill and a "widow's walk" or balcony. Also advertised, but not widely used, was a California Turbine windmill which featured a wheel with vertical shaft, under roof and protected from storms. This type was used more often in municipal water setups and at railroad water tanks. The ad is from Prairie Farmer.

Two windmill types

Looking at windmill manufacture and use historically, it is easy to recognize two streams of development. The Dutch type windmill originated in Europe and Asia and never enjoyed a great deal of acceptance in this country. On the other hand, the water-pumping small farm windmill is essentially an American invention.

The Dutch type deserves our attention because of its romantic past, but also because it really challenged the skills of the carpenter-artisans of the Middle Ages and on down through the 1800s. These were large mills used mostly to grind grain and lift water over dikes. They were massive in construction, built of heavy timbers arranged in ingenious ways. They were, in fact, almost in a class with the great baronial halls and cathedrals.

These windmills were probably first developed in England around the year 1100. The Crusaders brought them to the Middle East, although the Persians are believed to have had windmills of their own much earlier. Two characteristics of these huge mills catch the imagination of the person interested in engineering. One is the wheel which caught the wind. It was 60 or more feet high. It had four vanes framed in wood on which canvas sails were fastened. These were roped to the wooden frame as one would the sails of a ship, the amount of canvas being adjusted to the force of the wind.

The other engineering feature was the method used to turn these massive structures into the wind. This problem led first to a type of construction known as the post mill, a marvel in itself. Imagine a massive wheel with supports holding it high in the air, huge wooden gears and millstones, working space and in some cases living quarters for the miller and his family, all this hanging on a single post or pivot in such a way that the structure could be turned to face the wheel into the wind. The post mill was built of timbers, ingeniously mortised and angled for great strength. As the art of ironwork and blacksmithing developed, metal was adopted to supplement the timbers, but there were no steel I-beams to build around as we do in heavy construction today.

The prodigious task of pivoting a whole mill called for all kinds of levers and turning devices. The most common was probably a long pole to which oxen could be hitched.

After some years the design was changed so that only the cap (or cone) of the structure had to be pivoted. This meant moving the roof, wheel, and bearing mechanisms around to face the wind without disturbing the main building and foundations of the mill. This was a great improvement, but still required much muscle. Many ingenious methods were used to make the turning of the cap easier: a turning plate greased with tallow or other lubricant, a series of wooden rollers much like our modern roller bearings, even small truck wheels rolling on a platform.

Remember that this huge cap had to be so well secured that it did not blow away in a high wind! Leverage to turn the cap was accomplished usually with a large wooden spire (much like a modern telephone pole) which slanted to

the ground and often had at the end a wagon wheel. A horse, ox, or a group of men were employed to pull this great lever around so the vanes would be in the desired position to catch the wind.

There were no safety engineers in those days to tell you what you could or could not do. Obviously this was a dangerous machine. How to stop the wheel in a sudden high wind? How to adjust the speed so that good work might be done by the millstones? How to brace wooden frames and create mainbearings to carry the enormous load?

This was the Dutch type windmill that pioneers tried to transplant to America in colonial times. No wonder the transition did not go well. Quite a few windmills were built here, especially in Dutch communities where skills acquired in the old country were readily available. But all the drawbacks of the European mills turned up in this country, plus a few more. Illustrated in this book is a Dutch type mill which was erected in Minnesota — of all places — a couple hundred yards from the farmhouse in which the author was born. Minnesota was not noted for strong and reliable winds, nor were there many streams that lent themselves to watermills, but the demand around the turn of the century for power to grind grain was great.

This mill was built by a Swede named Magnus Miller who came to America in 1892, worked on the railroad for a year, and then decided to erect on a hill on my father's farm a Dutch type mill of a pattern widely used in southern Sweden. Miller had in his youth in the old country acquired skills in both construction and milling. He built the mill from scratch with timber cut in a nearby woodlot. The scale of the structure is hard to imagine today. The

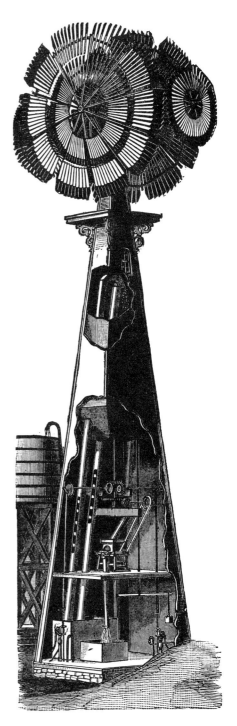

THE EFFORT to capture power from temperate winds resulted in all manner of double and auxiliary wheels. Some of them were self regulating and did not need a vane to hold them into the wind. Usually advertisements exaggerated the amount of work they could do.

29

wheel had a spread of 60 feet, supported by a massive frame of timber. The mill was of the cone type. The roof, the big wheel and its bearings were turned into the wind by a pole lever visible at the back in the picture. The lever which had the dimensions of a large telephone pole was manipulated at the ground level by several men or a team of horses. The mill worked well and did a lot of grinding for surrounding farmers in Dakota County, Minnesota. It could turn out as many as 800 sacks of feed in a long run of favorable wind, sometimes lasting 24 continuous hours.

Therein lay the problem, of course. It could run only when there was a brisk wind. And it was dangerous! My uncle, Aslak Alfson, one of the stalwart farm boys who helped Miller run his mill, said that fighting the big wheel to get canvas on and off the vanes was a mankilling job — literally mankilling when the wheel threatened to run away in a sudden storm.

The strenuous work, plus the unreliability of the wind in that part of Minnesota, caused Miller to shift after a few years from wind power to an old single cylinder Flour City tractor, which was almost as hard to handle as the mill. After ten years of this, Miller dismantled the mill and moved the stones and mechanism to the nearby town of Lakeville where he ground feed with gas power for another 10 years.

There are a few museum mills of the Dutch type (the Ford-Greenfield museum near Detroit, for one) in this country, but for practical purposes these mills have faded from the scene.

Not so with the smaller windmills of American design used primarily for pumping water. Beginning around 1860 and continuing past the turn of the century these farm windmills got a great deal of attention as a source of farmstead power. While their first job was to pump water, they were also used to grind feed, saw wood, chop fodder, run shop machinery, operate churns and washing machines, and do other farm jobs.

However, the range of uses touted in the advertisements of

the time did not pan out as hoped. There were several reasons for this. Winds were notoriously unreliable in many parts of the country. Windmill speeds were hard to regulate. Windmills were mostly mounted on 40-foot towers, and few farmers relished the job of oiling and maintaining the machinery at this great height. When alternate kinds of power presented themselves in the form of gas engines and electric motors, farmers were only too glad to abandon the creaky, cranky, noisy windmill.

Nevertheless, in the last half of the 1800s, before the age of small gas engines and electricity on the farm, there was intensive development of the windmill. Wooden wheels on wooden towers changed to metal wheels on metal towers. The troublesome problem of regulating speed was dealt with in several ways, as was the ever-present danger of the windmill running away in a severe windstorm and destroying itself. The problem of lubrication was reduced from once-a-week to once-a-year with enclosed gear cases. Multiwheel arrangements were invented to get more power from mild winds. Automatic governors were devised to reduce the area of wheel presented to the wind so as to hold down speed, or to cut out the wheel entirely in case of a sudden windstorm.

Even so the windmill did not get the precision engineering that was being applied to the steam engine, internal combustion engine and other basic farm machines. This may be corrected now that the energy sources are dwindling and we turn once more to the "free wind" as an alternate source of power for farm, household and factory.

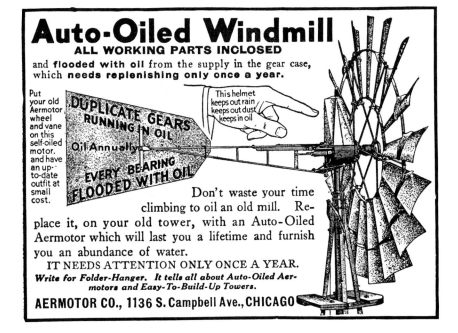

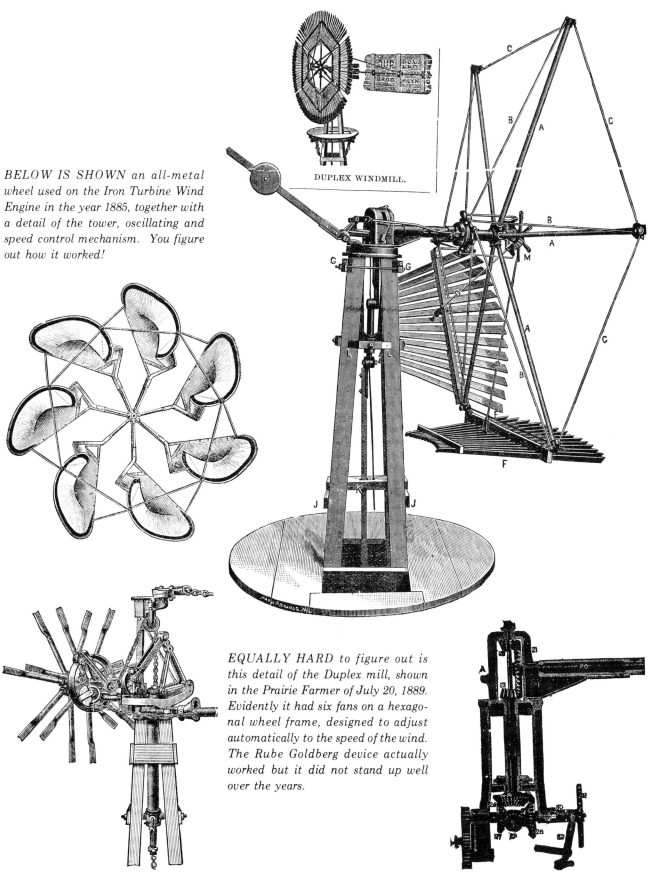

DUPLEX WINDMILL.

BELOW IS SHOWN an all-metal wheel used on the Iron Turbine Wind Engine in the year 1885, together with a detail of the tower, oscillating and speed control mechanism. You figure out how it worked!

EQUALLY HARD to figure out is this detail of the Duplex mill, shown in the Prairie Farmer of July 20, 1889. Evidently it had six fans on a hexagonal wheel frame, designed to adjust automatically to the speed of the wind. The Rube Goldberg device actually worked but it did not stand up well over the years.

AROUND THE TURN of the century there were at least 100 companies manufacturing farm windmills, most of them in the Middle West. They started out with both towers and wheels of wood but changed over slowly to both towers and wheels of galvanized metal. Some companies had a try at huge mills intended to pump water for railroads, municipalities, and even manufacturing plants. However, the larger users were in a position to change to steam and internal combustion engines, thereby driving the windmill companies into competing for the farm and ranch market. There was considerable export trade to livestock ranching areas in South America, Australia and even Africa, but the domestic trade was the heart of the business.

Railroads used them

There was a brief period around 1880 when the windmill was used, with only fair success, to pump water for railroads, small town water systems, and even for tenement complexes in cities. These were often huge wheels as much as 60 feet in diameter, mounted on municipal water tanks and on towers scattered along railroad rights-of-way to service the thirsty steam locomotives of an early day.

There was also some attempt toward running generators of electricity with wind power. Municipal plants abandoned this effort early in favor of steam engines, but farm type windchargers consisting of a two-blade airplane propellor, small generator and 32-volt battery were used quite extensively on farms in the 1920s. They may have a future today, but they will need a lot of improvement to handle the heavy electrical loads.

A man named David Halladay is credited with inventing the farm type windmill in 1854. This is probably somewhat in error because pumping water by wind was discussed at length in an issue of *Prairie Farmer* in 1853, reporting years of experimentation. A group of windmill manufacturers began operations in Batavia, Illinois, just after the Civil War, where a man named Thomas O. Perry did some really scientific research on the most effective height of tower and most efficient angle of vanes. Halladay worked especially to invent a wheel with automatic vanes that would actually stop of itself in a high wind and gradually take hold again as the wind declined.

In the latter half of the 1800s windmills did much of the work on farms. Farmers embraced them with great enthusiasm. The U.S. Wind Engine Company of America, one of the Batavia firms, sold wheel diameters ranging from 8 feet to 60 feet. An 8-footer cost $90, a 12-footer $130, and a 60-footer, used for commercial or municipal purposes, cost $3500. Writing in the *Country Gentleman* in the year 1889, E. E. Garfield of Kane County, Illinois, gave this testimonial:

"The writer's experience with windmills began about 20 years since with the earliest and most crude specimen of the genus windmill for the purpose of water pumping solely. Impossible of control as it was, running ever, stopping never . . . albeit it was in its day a great improvement on hand-pumping by 'armstrong' power.

"By this time an inventive Yankee had constructed a new pattern of 'wind engine' with folding sails which admitted of control in winds and calms. . . I was induced to try one of the new wind helpers which are now rearing their sails on many prairie farms. This gave better results, doing good work for about ten years. However it finally succumbed to time and use, and its place was supplied by a still later invention called the Goodhue wind engine, which promised not only to pump water but to grind feed, shell corn, cut fodder, and run various other machines. This has been in use on the writer's farm for about two and a half years, giving excellent service, both in pumping water for 100 head of livestock, summer and winter, grinding several thousand bushels of grain yearly, and in running other light machinery. . . .

IN THIS CHAPTER an attempt is made to show as many makes of windmills as possible, to give the reader some idea of the variety. Generally the mills are of two kinds, the plain flat wheel with movable vane which turned the wheel into the wind, or turned it sideways to the wind by means of a cable handled from the ground. The only way to slow the wheel was to turn it only partially into the wind. The more complicated wheels were composed of a series of fans which automatically adjusted to the speed of the wind and also turned the wheel into the wind without the presence of a vane or rudder. These were also designed to function with less wind force. The very complexity of these wheels was a source of trouble and led to their abandonment by most manufacturers.

Within a radius ten miles from my home there are now about 25 of these mills, mainly erected since my own and doing equally excellent service."

R. M. R. of Plymouth County, Iowa, also wrote in Country Gentleman in 1889: "We put in a Duplex 14-foot geared wind engine, at a cost for engine, grinder, etc., of $250. We furnished the tower, mill house, labor, etc., say at about $75 more, and we have been congratulating ourselves ever since. We are able to pump the water, grind the grain, and cut the fodder (with an 11 A Ross cutter) for 20 head of cattle, 18 horses and 40 hogs without any storage room at all. By having a storage tank for water, and a system of elevators and bins so as to let the grinder run at night, we could care for a much larger amount of stock. I think, in a brisk wind, our machine develops a power of three or four horses, and there are times when the machine would carry a much greater load . . . .

"I would like to experiment on its application to the generation of electricity and the storage of the same in batteries; this subject opens a field too vast for treatment in this article, but let us briefly consider. Here is a circle 14 feet in diameter developing a power of three or four horses or more; the current that moves it is miles in depth and hundreds of miles in width. . .take your pencil and figure up the total energy of the current flowing over a farm of 80 acres, over a section, over a county — the aggregate becomes inconceivable, and the much talked of water power of Niagara a mere bagatelle."

This was written in 1889. Would that we could summon this imaginative farmer-writer to help us with our energy problems today!

Renewed interest today

Work on harnessing the wind is actually going on today on an increasing scale, goaded on by the need for cheaper and renewable sources of energy. In reading the sketchy accounts one wonders if we have learned much since Perry made his experiments at Batavia. In 1945, before the energy crisis, a group built a wind generator on top of Grandpa's Knob near Rutland, Vermont. It had three 65-foot blades of stainless steel and a capacity of 1,250 kilowatts. The Central Vermont Public Service Corporation had agreed to take over the generator and supplement its output with purchased electricity when needed. After only a few weeks of operation the mill threw one of its big blades one windy night, and enthusiasm died out. Somehow, dealing with temperamental winds still dogs the experiments of the windmill makers.

In Europe, big wind generators have been built by Denmark, Germany, France and Russia with more or less success, mostly less according to scattered reports.

But talk about wind generators is building up and will undoubtedly produce something soon. William E. Heronemus, an engineering professor at the University of Massachusetts, has proposed a plan to build 300,000 huge wind generators and spread them over the American Great Plains from Canada to Mexico to take advantage of the steady winds that have done so well pumping water in the ranch country. These would have 50-foot blades and sky-scraping towers. The plan has found its way into the Congressional Record, but not much farther. There are now several projects under way, backed by university research and government money, but the results are still inconclusive.

Two windmills which will be probably the largest ever attempted are under construction now by General Electric. They will be 12 stories high and have fiberglass blades 200 feet long which are expected to make 30 or 40 revolutions per minute in winds of 18 miles per hour.

The government (Energy Research and Development Administration) is finally getting into the act with a ten million dollar subsidy for the General Electric windmills. ERDA is co-operating with Space Administration in selecting 18 sites for experimental windmills scattered over U. S. territory, including Hawaii and Puerto Rico. It is estimated that 55,000 square miles of the United States have sufficiently strong and constant winds to make generation of electricity by wind power practicable.

Suburbanites and acreage people in the country are installing the small scale windchargers that farmers abandoned when they got REA lines and loaded up their farmsteads with power hungry motors and appliances. This movement is handicapped by lack of good storage batteries and inability of the small chargers to handle heavy loads.

The demand is growing, the engineering world is stirring, and we will soon be giving the wind its due as a power source, following in the footsteps of imaginative farmers of 100 years ago.

IN THE TWENTIES with the growing demand for electricity on farms, windmills were fitted with generators and (on the ground) 32-volt batteries. The illustration just below is typical of these "windchargers" which utilized an airplane propellor or its equivalent. When REA lines began to cover the rural areas in the 1930s the windchargers were quickly abandoned because they simply could not furnish enough electric power for the modern farmstead.

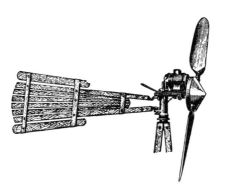

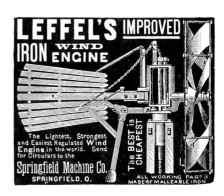

Billed-Magazin.

No. 32.]   Madison, Wisconsin den 10de Juli.   [1869.

Vindmøller

At raade over Skabningen og underlægge os dens Kræfter, er en Rettighed, som tilkommer Mennesket

ifølge Jehovahs Gavebrev til vor Stammefader. Lige fra Skabelsens Dage og indtil vore Tider har derfor Menneskets Stræben været rettet mod det Maal, at blive Herre over Naturkræfterne, og for hver ny Opda-

En Vindmølle.

Naturen Kræfter, der vil kunne udføre alle vore Arbei-der; kun at vi lærer at bruge dem og forstaar at benytte den Tjeneste, de tilbyde. Vandets Tyngde, Dampens

AT LEFT is a modern windmill in all its glory, the Star manufactured by Flint and Walling of Kendalville, Indiana. Modern research is zeroing in on larger mills which might furnish electricity for a whole town. Many energy engineers believe the day of the windmill has come full circle, and we will be paying more attention to this source of inexpensive and relatively inexhaustible power.

PLOWING AND HARVESTING BY STEAM
A SUCCESS.

I am now manufacturing the Celebrated **REMINGTON TRACTION ENGINE OR STEAM PLOW**, adapted to all kinds of heavy work usually done by mules or horses. A number of these Engines are now in use, giving entire satisfaction, for plowing and pulling Combined Harvesters. I have also patented and put into the field a successful **STEAM HARVESTER**, which the above cut represents, and can be seen on the ranch of Mr. J. H. Kester, St. Johns, Colusa county, harvesting 65 to 100 acres per day. Note what the owners say in testimonial:

ST. JOHNS, CALA., August 1, 1889.

DANIEL BEST—*Dear Sir:* You ask us to report how we like the Traction Engine and Steam Harvester purchased of you this season. We can only say that we are delighted with the purchase, and it is giving entire satisfaction. In other words, the whole outfit is a success. We never had better work done with any machine than we are doing with the Steam Harvester. We are using our 25-foot Header, traveling three miles per hour, cutting and threshing 65 to 100 acres per day. You can put us down for another rig for next season. Very truly yours,

KESTER & PETERS.

If you are interested in Steam Plowing and Steam Harvesting, go and investigate for yourself and be convinced. The following parties are using my Traction Engines and Harvesters, who will take pleasure in showing them up: J. S. Butler, W. Fennell, Tehama, Tehama county; Henry Best, Yuba City, Sutter county; and Kester & Peters, St. Johns, Colusa county. These last parties are running a complete steam outfit, consisting of Traction Engine and Steam Harvester. For further description, prices, etc., address

Daniel Best Agricultural Works,
SAN LEANDRO, CAL.

STEAM POWER

Most romantic of all

The windmill and the water-wheel, both of ancient origin, were efforts to harness two readily available natural forces for the service of man. As related to agriculture they were relatively crude machines relying on the art of woodworkers and blacksmiths. They never attained great stature in the mechanical age that began to take shape early in the 1800s.

The treadmill and the sweep power came into being to meet a growing demand for rotary or belt power, utilizing the weight and energy of the traditional beasts of burden, ox, horse, and mule. They too were simple machines that served a useful purpose in an emerging machine age in need of separate power units.

It was not until steam power was invented that mechanization really began to move forward rapidly. Steam kindled a flurry of mechanical inventiveness that powered the industrial revolution and laid the groundwork for the almost complete mechanization of agriculture that we see about us today in America. At one time around 90 percent of people in any given area had to put in most of their time as farmers wresting a living from the soil. Now the proportion of farmers actually engaged in tilling the soil is less than five percent in the United States and other advanced countries.

This figure may be somewhat misleading in that we are inclined to forget all the people engaged in furnishing the technology for agriculture. Nevertheless, the change in farming has been profound, and the substitution of mechanical power for human energy is the key to this change.

Steam had its advantages in that it required a somewhat simpler level of engineering than was later needed for internal combustion engines and electrical motors. It also used fuel that was readily available without processing; first wood, then coal, and later, on the plains of Minnesota and the Dakotas, straw. These fuels were cheap, and so was the other ingredient in the making of steam, water. Water heavily laden with lime and other minerals could be a problem, of course, but steam engine operators found ways of dealing with these pollutants.

Steam generated by coal was absolutely essential in the early years of the industrial revolution. Even as the textile mills of England moved rapidly to use the engines perfected by James Watts and others in the late 1700s, other inventors got very busy trying to make steam take on some of the heavy work of farming. England was a hotbed of steam development for agriculture from the beginning of the 1800s. There were

large scale farmers in the British Isles who were well financed and had fields of a size that would accommodate large equipment. The English manufacturers naturally spilled over into the United States and Canada — also Egypt, Australia and other parts of the empire where there were large expanses of farmland.

Steam engines were utilized all over the world for belt power by 1850. Soon after that there was a concerted effort to harness steam for plowing both in England and America. The inventors and manufacturers made the mistake of building too big engines that could be used only on large fields.

Steam plowing flourished for a time on the American Great Plains, in the delta country of Louisiana, and in the wheat country of the western states, but mostly steam engines settled down to the job of threshing grain grown with horsepower. It was not until the small gasoline-powered tractor was developed in the first quarter of the 1900s that farmers really abandoned horses for mechanical power in virtually all farm operations.

One of the first patents ever granted in England, 1618, went to David Ramsey and Thomas Wildgoss for a device to utilize steam to cultivate soil. This proves nothing except that even

TODAY'S FARMER will find it almost unbelievable that early efforts to mechanize farming would spawn an impractical idea such as stationing big steam engines on opposite sides of a field and snaking a plow back and forth by cable. That's what happened in England around the year 1850. It is believed that as many as 1000 cable outfits were built and sold, but very few of them found their way to the United States. One such rig was tried in North Dakota, but it took too much cable to cover the big fields. There had to be a better way!

FRONTISPIECE.

STEAM-PLOUGHING.

40

at that early date inventors were dreaming up ideas along the line of mechanical farming. However, by the 1760s James Watt had invented a workable steam engine. The problem of moving a heavy engine across soft ground was being explored in patents as early as 1770. In 1786 Thomas Jefferson made a trip to England and came back impressed by the steam engines in use there.

By the year 1800 English inventors were off to the races, with American farmer-inventors participating either in the English developments or launching patents of their own. The first farm engines were strictly stationary, on masonry bases. Then they were mounted on skids or wheels and called portable. Such engines inaugurated steam cultivation, stationed at opposite ends of a field, with plows and other farm implements drawn back and forth by cables on windlasses. Even after the power was applied to traction wheels so that engines became self-propelled, steering

was left to a team of horses hitched on the front of the engine. The full-fledged steam tractor, self-propelled and steered, did not become common until the 1880s.

Cable plow outfits, known as "steam tackle," consisting of an engine for each end of the field, reversible plows, windlass and cable, were cumbersome, expensive and required much manpower. In spite of that at least 1000 such rigs were made and sold. In the currency of the time an outfit cost around $5000. Even after ingenious arrangements of pulleys made it possible to operate with only one engine, the steam tackle had many drawbacks. Metal cable was expensive and heavy to handle. It took a lot of it to go twice across a large field.

There is a record of a cable outfit being invented by a South Carolina man, E. C. Billinger, as early as 1833, but the "tackle" most widely known and used was invented by John Fowler of England in 1852. He also took out U. S. patents some years later. By 1856

the Congress of the United States was sufficiently impressed by the Fowler steam rig to permit its importation free of duty. Fowler sold 35 sets of "steam tackle" in England and Scotland in 1860. Three years later he turned out 600 sets, many for export. By 1867 there were 200 sets in Egypt, but only two were reported in the United States, one in Louisiana and one in Illinois. Later there were cable sets in North Dakota and Canada but they made little headway in the wide open wheat country.

Even while cable outfits were being built and sold, numerous patents were issued both in England and America for steam plow engines that could move across fields. Invariably, the problem was to get heavy equipment over soft ground without bogging down, or using up all of the engine's power simply to move the machine. J. Boydell of England patented in 1846 an engine that laid its own plank track in a most awkward manner. Henry Corning of England had an engine that could

IN AN ATTEMPT to make the cable system of plowing more efficient, inventors set up ingenious systems of pulleys to permit plows and other farm implements to be operated by one steam engine in a corner of the field. The Savage system, as late as 1880, figured out a way to wind the cables on drums in the drivewheels of the engine, thus combining the cable system with an engine that did not have to be moved by horses. It was a lost cause however. Use of steam on a big scale in farming had to await the self-propelled engine which was already taking shape in both England and America soon after mid-century.

41

travel under its own power in 1850, but that was all it could do! T. H. Burridge of St. Louis, Missouri, built an engine in 1860 that got its traction from a giant cylinder ten feet wide and ten feet high, but this engine evidently died a-borning. John W. Fawkes of Lancaster, Pennsylvania, built a plow engine in 1859 which was among the most successful of the early rigs.

The *Report of the Commissioner of Patents*, forerunner of the *U. S. Yearbook of Agriculture*, published in 1859 evaluations of both the Fowler steam tackle originating in England and the Fawkes steam plow built in Pennsylvania.

The Fowler plow: "The engine in use was upon one side of the field, and was called a stationary engine. It was drawn to the field by horses, but had powers of locomotion sufficient to run itself along the headland. The plow was drawn toward the engine by a wire rope which passed across the field, around a pulley made fast at the opposite headland. This pulley was held by what was called an anchor, which anchor was in the shape of a low cart or car, loaded heavily with stones. . . . This anchor was drawn along the opposite headland by a windlass, worked by a man in a direction at right angles to the furrow, so that the strain upon the pulley was at right angles with the track of the wheels. . . . The force employed in this operation, as I witnessed it, consisted of the engineer who remained by the engine, a boy to carry coal, one man upon the plow to manage it, another man who rode part time on the plow, and who ran along before it to remove pulleys or rollers over which the rope traversed, another man to tend the windlass and anchor, and another to keep the rope in place with a crowbar, that it might wind properly around the drums of the engine."

In the same publication is a partial description of the American-made Fawkes steam plow: "In the middle of the forward section of a platform stands an upright boiler which is 6½ feet high and 4 feet in diameter, the fire-box and ash-pit being of course below the level of the platform. . . . The cylinders are horizontal, 9 inches in diameter and 15 inches stroke, and are placed on each side of the boiler. The pistons communicate motion not to the sidewheels but to a drum or roller 6 feet in diameter and 6 feet long which, as the sides of the platform overhang it, is comparatively out of sight. . . . The bow is supported by a body-bolt on a truck composed of two iron guidewheels 3½ feet in diameter and 15 inches broad. The truck moves freely like the front wheels of a chaise and is controlled by a steering wheel in charge of the engineer, so the whole machine is turned as readily and as short as a farm wagon. The entire length of the machine is 18 feet, its weight with water and fuel 10 tons; and cost including donkey engine and pump about $4000. . . . The plows, eight in number, are attached to one frame, which is suspended by chains, passing over grooved pulleys, in two beams, projecting from the seat of the engine. The frame of plows is drawn by other chains, which are attached to the underside of the frame of the engine."

Surprisingly, one of the best descriptions of a cable plowing outfit was written by a man from Fargo, North Dakota, to a Boston newspaper, describing the operation of such a plow rig in his state. *Prairie Farmer* quoted the letter in 1882:

"Two enormous traction engines are placed about 300 to 500 yards apart. Beneath each engine and bolted to the boiler is a steel drum

WHEN ENGINES became self-propelled, operators were immediately confronted by the problem of moving heavy machines across soft ground. J. Boydell's invention, shown as Plate 29 in the 1867 Yearbook of America, shows an attempt to have the engine lay down its own track of planks. Could this be interpreted as the first application of the crawler principle? The lower engraving, printed as Plate 18 in the 1970 Yearbook, reveals a somewhat smaller steam tractor with wooden drums for wheels. The early yearbooks of the U. S. Department of Agriculture devoted a good deal of space to British inventions in steam farming, and its editors and writers were quick to report and analyze the efforts of inventors in this country working along similar lines. It was generally agreed that the enormous weight of the early steam tractors greatly limited their usefulness.

J. BOYDELL'S INVENTION. (Patented in 1846.)

LORD DUNMORE'S STEAM PLOW.

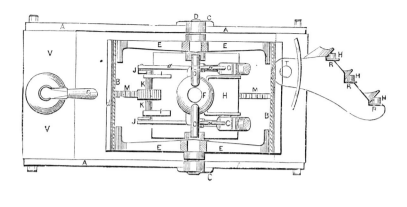

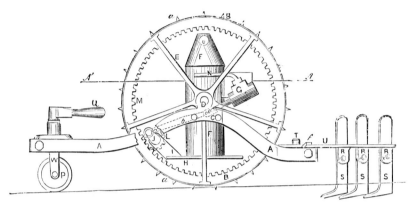

AMERICAN INVENTORS were quick to get into the act of designing a steam tractor that would meet conditions of American farming. Here are patent drawings of two schemes published in the 1867 Yearbook of Agriculture. Burridge was a St. Louis man who conceived the idea of an engine inside of a huge drum. J. W. Fawkes of Philadelphia had a more successful steam plow which was actually built and sold. It used drums for locomotion but mounted the engine and the plows outside. Both patents utilized a front wheel for steering. These are simplified patent drawings and do not give a really good idea of the finished machine.

T H. BURRIDGE'S IMPROVEMENT. (Patented July 31, 1860)

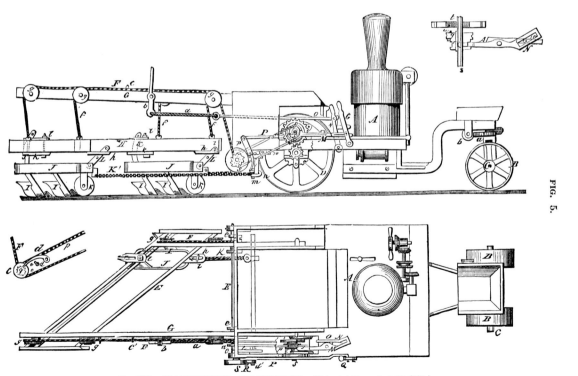

J. W. FAWKIS'S PLOUGH. (Patented December 13, 1859.)

PLATE XXXII.

FIG. 5.

about five feet in diameter. To these drums is attached a steel cable about three-quarters of an inch in diameter, 500 yards long and capable of sustaining a weight of 30 tons which drags the plow to and fro across the field. The plow is a framework of iron resting on two wheels; on each side of the frame are firmly fixed six plows with colters that cut six furrows 16 inches wide each time the machine crosses the field. On arrival of the plow at the end of the furrow the gauge changes position and the plows that have been in the air are lowered and ready to start back. . . . Each engine is about 40 horsepower and weighs about 16 tons. . . . The plow will break from 25 to 35 acres per day, according to the soil, location, and lay of the land."

The above descriptions are merely sketchy excerpts from the lengthy discussions published in the yearbooks and magazines of the time, all combining to give an impression of the unbelievably huge, clumsy and heavy machines that inaugurated steam plowing. Even so, these mechanical monsters, reminiscent of the dinosaurs, were embraced with some enthusiasm by the larger scale farmers in England and America. It is reported that by 1867 there were around 3000 steam plowing rigs, either cable or traction, scattered over the British colonies and America.

STEAM PLOWING was not limited to the conventional moldboard plows. The British also tried out various "diggers" which were somewhat similar to rototillers used today. The Derby digger (1879) that traveled sideways crab-fashion was actually put on the market. Critics were quick to point out that an expensive steam engine should be useful for other things besides tilling the soil.

An evaluation of the weaknesses and possibilities of the steam rigs was consequently published in the Report of the Commissioner of Agriculture in 1867, five years after the department was established on its own. Professor J. Brainard wrote:

"An engine, to become a profitable investment, must be constructed as to be made useful in other departments of farm labor than merely ploughing and cultivating the crop. It must be capable of adaptation for driving a threshing machine, sawing wood, grinding provender, churning, washing, pumping water, indeed, all kinds of labor now performed either by hand or animal power.

"If steam ploughing is ever to be made practicable, if the steam engine is to become generally usable upon the farm, it can only be at moderate expense. The errors in attempts yet made in steam ploughing have arisen, perhaps, from making the steam engine too heavy, and on too large a scale."

An English Steam Digger.—The London Agricultural Gazette describes a combined traction engine and steam digging machine, manufactured by a Norfolk establishment and shown in the accompanying cut:

It consists of an ordinary farm traction engine, but underneath the stoking platform is arranged the digging apparatus; this can be disconnected, so that the machine can be used for threshing and other farm purposes as well as for digging. There are three forks which enter the ground alternately; the total width which they dig over all extends a little beyond the total width over the wheels. They are made in two sizes, the smallest is 5 h.p., and digs 7 ft. wide over all; and the larger is of 8 h.p., with two cylinders (compounded), by which means a great saving of water and fuel is effected, which is a point of considerable importance. When the digging forks are in work, wherever the digger travels they dig up the wheel marks which would otherwise be made by the machine, and it thereby overcomes one of the chief objections to the steam plowing machines.

This digger is said to have been thoroughly tested on all soils, and is much less costly in the outset than the steam plow used in England, while its working expenses in the field are stated to be only half as great.

Darby's Steam Digger, turning up 16 feet at each turn.

THE PARVIN STEAM plow was one of the first machines
in the United States to attract wide attention. R. C. Parvin
was a Philadelphia man who immediately saw the great
potential for sales in the Middle West. He tried hard to
promote his steam plow in Illinois, but farmers were skeptical after watching the Fawkes plow win prizes for performance in Indiana and Illinois and then begin gradually
fading from the scene. Shown here is an unusual display
of the simplified drawing that accompanied the Parvin
patent application in 1871, and a detailed engraving of the
complete engine published in Prairie Farmer. Note the
crawler principle used here too.

PLATE XXI.

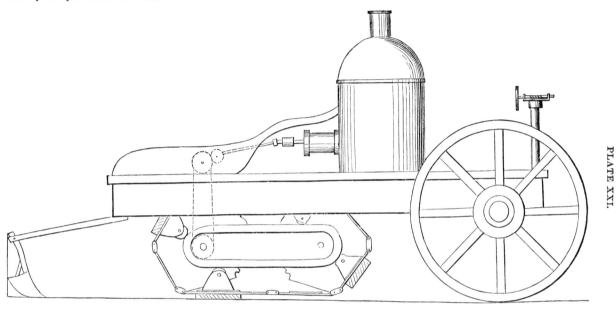

PARVIN'S TRACTION ENGINE.

[Patented October 10, 1871.]

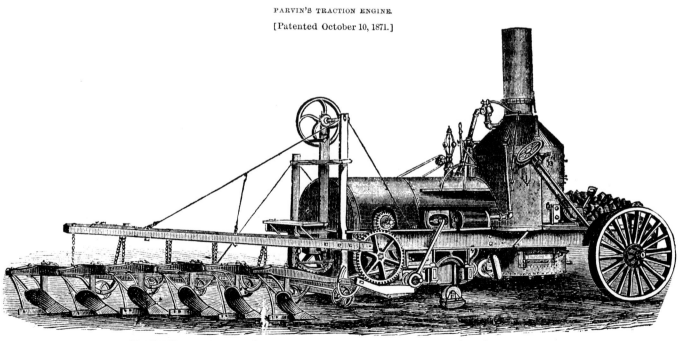

PARVIN'S STEAM MOTOR, FOR FARM AND ROAD WORK.

STATIONARY *steam engines were widely used in America all the time that traction power was being tried out in the various stages of development. Stationaries were used for threshing, sawing wood, ginning cotton, crushing cane, pumping water, and running grist mills. These two illustrations are from The Country Gentleman of 1856 and the Prairie Farmer of 1862, indicating considerable advance in the engines before the Civil War.*

Steam Engines on the Farm.

Portable Steam Engine for Farm Purposes.

Steam engines are in common use in Great Britain for farm purposes ; and in all the modern farmeries of England provision is made as regularly for the steam engine as for the threshing machine, chaff-cutter, &c. As yet they have but rarely been employed for farm purposes in this country. We cannot doubt however, but that the time is rapidly approaching when our large farmers will find their employment a profitable investment, and we take pleasure in copying the following account of the introduction of one into the farm operations of our friend J. A. HUMPHREYS, Esq., of Versailles, Ky. It is from a letter written by him to one of the editors of the *Valley Farmer*, from which paper we copy it.

You request me in your letter to furnish you with an account of my " Portable Steam Engine for Farm Purposes," which I do with pleasure, fully assured that the substitution of such a steam power, on all our farms of moderate size, is only a *question of time*.

The Engine as yet has been tried only under the most unfavorable circumstances. Standing out doors, entirely unprotected, the weather intensely cold, the wood green, the machinery all new, many little advantages not given it,—yet it more than equalled my expectations, and gave entire satisfaction to all who saw it work. I tried it threshing grain with perfect success—not using more than one-third the amount of steam which was kept up, without the least difficulty— nor did there appear to be the least danger of setting fire to the straw. I then tried it crushing corn in the cob with one of Pitt's Crushers, which I have had in use for the last four years, and though it was dull, and many of the teeth broken, with *such* an application of power, I never saw better nor faster work done. I also tried the engine cutting straw, corn stalks and hay with equal success, using one of Sinclair's 13 inch cutters. I was satisfied that the engine could have driven the three machines all at the same time.

A. N. WOOD & CO.'S PORTABLE STEAM ENGINE FOR FARM PURPOSES.

THE ENGINE shown above may be the first of the American portables. This is the Forty-Niner designed and produced by A. M. Archambault of Philadelphia. Archambault engines were sold in several sizes, 4, 10 and 30 horsepower. Also shown on this page are an upright from around 1870 and a Gaar-Scott engine from 1871. Gaar-Scott was destined to be one of the biggest producers of steam engines.

Smaller, stationary steam engines were built and adapted for farm use even while the behemoths were being developed, but even they were too big for such tasks as pumping water and running washing machines. They were mostly used for threshing grain, sawing wood, ginning cotton, crushing sugar cane, and other operations, usually on larger farms. They graduated from stationary bases to skids, and then to wheels, requiring oxen or horses to move them from job to job.

There were portables on wagon wheels as early as 1849. A. M. Archambault of Philadelphia built a four horsepower portable and a larger ten-horse engine in that year. J. I. Case, later to become the greatest of all manufacturers of steam tractors and threshing machines, also built an eight horsepower, horse-drawn portable in 1849. However, Case entered the field cautiously, buying and adapting patents, moving into steam gradually as farmers became used to this new form of power. While Case dominated the steam manufacturing field before the end of the century, he continued to make sweep horsepowers to go with some of his threshing machines until the late 1890s.

While the British pioneered the use of steam in farming it was inevitable that the biggest market would be in the colonies and dominions where there were larger expanses of farmland to be possessed and exploited. The British continued to manufacture steam outfits both for their own use and for export, but the center of steam engine manufacturing soon shifted to America where inventors and manufacturers had been cutting their teeth on harvesters, threshing machines and all manner of farm implements since before the Civil War.

Plowman John Deere and Harvester Cyrus McCormick took their time about being drawn into the engine business, but others such as Jerome I. Case of Wisconsin, Obed Hussey of Maryland, Hiram and John Pitts of Maine, Abraham and Jonas Gaar of Indiana began making or handling portable steam engines at mid-century. By 1875 John Nichols of Michigan, Meinard Rumley of Indiana, George Frick of Pennsylvania, Joseph Enright and H. W. Rice of California, had their names on engines.

By 1875 steam for threshing (and on the Great Plains and in the West for plowing) was widely accepted. Indeed, there were so many American manufacturers that British imports dwindled to almost nothing. This was true even of the Canadian wheat provinces which somehow attached themselves to machines and methods used in the United States.

The Homestead Law of 1862 probably had as much to do as anything with placing limitations on the use of steam in American agriculture. The farm unit from the east coast to the Rockies became more or less fixed at 80 or 160 acres of land, much too small to support a steam outfit. Many pioneer farmers promptly acquired more land, but this was the exception rather than the rule. Family farmers, as we later called them, stuck with their horses as the principal source of farm power until around 1915-25 when the small gas tractor gave them a practical alternate. They thereby bypassed the steam age, except for one important operation, the threshing

SOME OF THE REASONS WHY WE HAVE A SUPERIOR ENGINE.

Boilers—Are made of the best government-inspected boiler plate.

Flues—Are American lap-welded and of the best practical size. Longer than those usually used, and more of them.

Economy—Will make more steam with less fuel than others.

Hauling—Large truck wheels lessening the draft in drawing.

Blower—On each Engine, that with wood or coal raise steam easily.

Pump—A direct acting force pump, cage valves, and cannot get out of order.

Governor—Judson's Patent, with lever and weight attachments, controlling the speed of the Engine by simply moving the weight on the lever.

Heater and Cylinder—Are mounted so as to equalize the weight on the axle, and not put as some are, on one side, making the danger of capsizing and hauling very great.

Fire Box—Its construction the best to ensure strength, durability and capacity for generating steam.

Steam—Is made in less time than with ordinary Engines.

Explosion—Need not be feared if our directions are followed.

Brake—Attached to each Engine; no extra charge made.

Cleaning—Is easily done through the hand holes at suitable places.

Wheels—Have adjustable flange hubs; are light, strong and high.

No Danger from Fire—The escape steam discharges into the smoke stack, preventing with the Spark Arrester we attach, any danger from fire.

Important—Pure water without any admixture of whisky is all that is needed to make steam for the J. I. Case & Co. Engine; a fact engineers will do well to remember.

Dimensions of Engine.

Description	Eight H. P.	Ten H. P.	Fift'n H. P.
Diam of Cylinder.	6½ in.	7 in.	8 in.
Stroke of Cylinder ..	12 in.	12 in.	12 in
Length of Boiler....	105 in.	117 in.	136 in.
Diam. of Boiler	26 in.	26 in.	30 in.
Length of Fire Box..	33 in.	33 in.	34 in.
Width of Fire Box..	24 in.	24 in.	29½ in.
Height of Fire Box..	29 in.	29 in.	35 in.
Number of Flues ...	Forty.	Forty.	Fifty.
Length of Flues.....	60 in.	72 in.	84 in.
Diam. of Flues......	2 in.	2 in.	2 in.
Diam. of Fly Wheel.	42 in.	42 in.	48 in.
Revolutions ⅌ minute	180	180	165

WE furnish with each Engine sold, one poker, one flue scraper and rod, one oil can, one combination wrench, one set clamps (wood), one funnel for filling boiler, 1 set whiffletrees and neckyoke.

J. I. CASE built his first steam engine in 1870, a portable now preserved in the Smithsonian Institute. The engine illustrated in the Almanac of 1878 was one of his later portables. That same year he put out his first self-propelled engine. One of the things Jerome I. Case did best was to measure the reaction of his customers. He spent a lot of his time in the field, visiting farmers and setting up dealerships.

AGRICULTURAL STEAM ENGINES.

EQUALED BY NONE IN COMBINED MERITS OF
CAPACITY, ECONOMY, DURABILITY, SIMPLICITY AND PERFECTION.
ADAPTED ESPECIALLY TO
GRAIN THRESHING, WOOD AND SHINGLE SAWING, COTTON GINNING

HERE ARE some more portable engines from the 1870s. Wood, Taber and Morse of Eaton, New York, were prominent manufacturers of other farm machinery. Westinghouse was a comparatively new name in the business, destined to become familiar to present day Americans.

of the grain. It was steam threshing that gave every farm boy in the East and Middle West his taste of the romance of steam, savored even today as an exciting memory.

It must be recorded here, however, that behemoths which inaugurated the age of steam had their day. Large operators in the semi-arid wheat plains where smaller farmers failed bought the big plow engines in considerable numbers. Engineers got around the problem of traction with huge drive wheels and later by adopting the crawler principle. Large steam engines, burning coal and pulling plows of 10 to 20 bottoms, blackened the prairies of Saskatchewan and Manitoba, North and South Dakota, Montana, Nebraska, and the Far West. There were some very large farms in these regions. Most famous, perhaps, were the Bonanza Farms of North Dakota which were actually bigger operations than some of the corporation farms we watch with apprehension today.

Even in Big Sky country most farmers were relatively small and got most of their power from horses. For these farmers steam excelled not for plowing but for threshing. The threshing rig was king and queen among all farm machines. The steam engine and the separator were inseparable. Between them they wrote the romantic chapter that is now celebrated at scores of steam reunions and demonstrations all over the country.

The threshing crew and rig were described in a previous volume in this series, *"Farm Inventions in the Making of America."* In the Cornbelt where farms were relatively small the threshing rig consisted usually of a steam engine of 15 to 25 horsepower, a separator of 40 to 50-inch cylinder width, a tank wagon for hauling water and

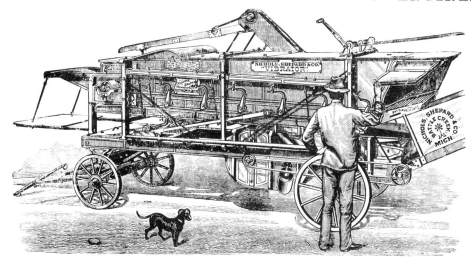

SCORES OF manufacturers got into the steam business during the portable (horse-drawn) period which lasted into the early 1880s. The top ads on this page are by two firms that headquartered in Indianapolis. A. B. Farquhar was prominent in the early history of steam farm engines. Incidentally, sawing lumber was one of the most profitable uses of engines, ranking only second to threshing.

a box or straw wagon for hauling fuel. The crew consisted of engineer, separator man (who was usually the boss), a waterboy and a fireman. If straw was burned, the fireman was kept very busy from 3:30 a.m. (it took several hours to get up steam) until evening darkness, forking straw into the firebox with a slow steady motion. If coal or wood was burned, the engineer sometimes doubled as fireman. The waterboy hauled water from nearby creeks, lakes, wells, often pushing his team at a dead run. Low water was a dangerous condition at the engine.

Rigs were usually owned by professional threshermen, who might also do some farming. The engineer had some schooling in steam engineering, or had previously run industrial engines. The separator man was wise in the ways of machinery adjustment, belts, lubrication. He also knew something about arithmetic and the psychology of dealing with over-particular farmers, and mischievous crews who were not above playing a few tricks, such as clogging the machine to get an unscheduled siesta in the shade of their wagons. The fireman and water boy were strictly roustabout types who worked hard and drifted from job to job.

In the Cornbelt it took only a day or two to do the threshing on the individual farm, so moving the big rig was an important maneuver, usually accomplished at night to save daylight during the precious weeks from the middle of August to middle of October. Some farmers preferred to thresh right out of the shock. This called for a group of farmers cooperating in change work to furnish ten bundle racks and two grain boxes, manned by some 15 men or husky boys, plus at least 24 horses. Smaller crews were required for threshing stacked grain, usually done later in the fall.

THE TRANSITION from portable to self-propelled and self-steered engines occurred in the late 1870s and continued through the 1880s. The engine at top is self-propelled but steered by horses. It bears the name of Russell of Massillon, Ohio, destined to be an important name in steam well into the next century. Below is one of the earliest J. I. Case engines that was both self-propelled and self-steered.

RUSSELL & CO.'S FARM ENGINE, WITH TRACTION ATTACHMENT.

53

THE ENGINE at left turned up recently at the Mt. Pleasant steam engine show in Iowa. The author failed to get an identification as to make. The engine below was one of the forerunners of the Buffalo Pitts line. The two Pitts brothers started as thresher manufacturers in the East. They split up into two lines, known in the trade as Buffalo Pitts and Chicago Pitts.

THE PITTS AGRICULTURAL WORKS, BUFFALO, N. Y.

54

Moving the big rig called for considerable skill on the part of the engineer. Plank bridges that crossed most creeks and rivers simply could not hold up a steam engine. The outfit went cross-country when possible, bypassed bridges by fording streams, and exercised the privilege of taking down fences to facilitate short-cuts. It was a moment of high excitement when the snorting monster entered the farmyard. More than one gatepost had to be sacrificed to its majestic progress.

Livestock farmers valued their strawstacks and wanted them as close to the farm buildings as possible. It took some doing to maneuver the machines around farm buildings and to "set" the rig in such a manner that bundle and grain wagons, water wagon and straw wagon could be moved in and out freely.

Thresher drive belts were 50 or 60 feet long, which meant that the engineer had to position the cumbersome separator with care, then back off a measured distance, all the time lining up the pulleys so that the belt would run true. The engineer who could back into perfect alignment on the first pass would get spontaneous applause from the watching crews and spectators.

Out in the wheat country there was plenty of room. This was fortunate because the engines and separators were usually bigger, and a cook wagon was added to the threshing train that moved from farm to farm. In the Cornbelt only four or five men came with the rig. The rest of the 20 or so needed to handle the threshing were local farmers. In the Dakotas the crew traveling with the rig might number 20, including a couple of cooks. The host farmer and his near neighbors were often kept busy hauling the grain to

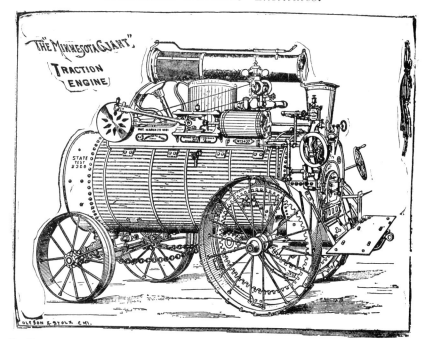

Minnesota Thresher Mfg. Co.,
STILLWATER, MINN.
MANUFACTURERS OF
THRESHERS, ENGINES, HORSE POWERS, AUTOMATIC STACKERS, SELF FEEDERS, ELEVATORS, BAGGERS AND MEASURES.

END FOR CATALOGUE SHOWING LATE IMPROVEMENTS.

IN THE 1890s Minnesota emerged as a very important center for the manufacture of threshing and other farm machinery. This was probably due to the fact that the Twin Cities were the gateway to the lucrative North Dakota and Canada market for all kinds of grain handling machines. The famous Minneapolis line was started at Stillwater, as can be seen from this Farmers' Institute bulletin of 1894.

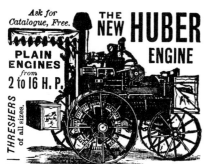

town. Feeding the entire crew was too big a task for the farmer's wife, so that became the responsibility of the owner-operator of the rig.

There was more than a little danger connected with steam engines and all that went with them. Explosions were surprisingly few, considering the conditions under which engines were operated — unskilled help, cross country travel, boilers caked with mineral deposits from bad water, freezing temperatures. There were enough mishaps, however, that tales were told from other years and other places, and engines were held in considerable awe. More likely accidents than explosion were belts flying off pulleys, feeder knives biting into stones or pitchforks, and of course the constant worry over skittish horses and runaway teams.

Fear of steam without doubt played an important part in farmers' reluctance to accept these engines as regular farm equipment, and accounted for much of the alacrity with which they jumped all the way from horses to gas engines, thus bypassing steam in the farm mechanization process. Along with fear of explosions came the fear of fire. Snorting engines would throw sparks from their stacks in spite of screened bonnets. Spilled sparks from the firebox were an ever present danger, especially when the rig was on the move. Fields were often tinder dry around harvest and threshing time.

Farmers lived in the midst of danger and usually took it in their stride. After all, the old sweep horsepowers, with their exposed gears and tumbling rods, had accounted for many a lost arm or leg.

Steam engine history

This book will not do justice to the technical and statistical aspects of the steam development during the years when this source of power played a decisive role in agricultural growth in America, roughly from 1875 to 1920. The latter date will surprise many who assume that the gas tractor had taken over much earlier. The fact is that steam power continued to thresh American grain crops for many years after the internal combustion tractors were well established in other farm operations.

Students of steam power on the farm can get the story in greater detail, properly documented, in what is probably the best publication on the subject, *Steam Power on the American Farm*, by Professor Raymond M. Wik of Mills College, Oakland, California (University of Pennsylvania Press, Philadelphia, 1953).

A quick recap of the trials and tribulations of steam is included here for students of farm power in general.

First engines used on American farms were, as has been pointed out, stationary, patterned after similar engines used in industry. They were fired by wood, coal, and occasionally oil. They had upright boilers with the cylinder, crank and belt wheel unit sometimes separate and distant from the boiler. As steam power multiplied its uses, it became desirable for the engine to be portable, first on skids and later on wheels. This meant abandoning the masonry foundation and putting both boiler and engine in the same wood or metal frame. These relatively small portables were made in a size ranging from four horsepower

HERE ARE TWO road locomotives from the 1880s, so-called because they were used to haul all kinds of freight, even mail, over the pioneer trails and highways. They did succeed in giving the railroads something of a scare.

AVELING & PORTER'S ROAD AND FARM LOCOMOTIVE AND TRAIN.

IMPROVED HIGH SPEED ROAD LOCOMOTIVE, FOR POSTAL SERVICE.

BY 1889 when this engraving was made, the steam tractor was beginning to assume the shape and style which characterized this machine right down to 1920s when its manufacture tapered off. This is the Geiser Peerless. Geiser didn't get started until 1889, but the company was destined to be second only to Case in the number of engines turned out during the age of steam.

to ten. The first portable, drawn by horses or oxen, is believed to have been built by A. L. Archambault in Philadelphia in 1849. From that date until around 1875, portables were the order of the day, used exclusively for belt work, mostly grain threshing.

There were dozens of manufacturers, most of whom were already in the reaper and threshing machine business. Prominent among these were the George Frick Company in the East, Russell, Gaar-Scott, and J. I. Case from Ohio westward. When the portables were pressed into service for itinerant threshing, the extra team or two of horses required to move the rig quickly became a pain-in-the-neck for threshermen. A good sized rig needed four horses to move the engine, two horses for the water tank, and another team or two for the threshing machine.

Nevertheless, it took until around 1880 for the inventors to come up with a reasonably good self-propelled engine. While the RPM at the piston was relatively slow, judged by later gas engine standards, it was still a long way down to the two or four miles per hour expected from the big drive wheels. Chains as well as trains of gear wheels were both used. Gears were found most practical because they were safer on downhill runs when gravity tended to take over and throw off the drive chains, with disastrous results. Oddly enough, inventors worked on and solved the problem of self-propulsion before they got around to building a steering gear. The odd combination of an engine that moved under its own power, with a tongue up front to steer with, was the rule for several years.

In the author's home community

STEAM-PLOWING, BY THE GEISER M'F'G. CO.'S OUTFIT, WAYNESBORO, PA.

in Minnesota there is a story still going around about a farmer who owned one of these engines. On one occasion he had gotten up steam to move to a new location nearby. Alone at the time, he called his wife from the farmhouse to come and help. He instructed her as to what levers to move while he went forward to hold up the tongue and thereby steer to the desired location. They had just gotten going when the safety valve blew. The lady screamed, jumped off the platform, and ran for the house, leaving her husband struggling with the steering pole of a moving machine. In desperation he steered the engine into a circle and hung on until it ran out of steam and stopped of its own accord.

Case built his first self-propelled engine in 1876 with a tongue for steering. Two years later he had an engine which could be steered by the engineer. The steering mechanism consisted of a worm gear, a drum and chains to the front wheels. This type of gear was still being used on big tractors 40 years later.

The first "complete" engines, self-propelled, self-steered, and capable of forward and reverse travel, made their appearance around 1880. The steam boom in agriculture was ready to get under way.

When farm engines began to move under their own power and under control of the engineer, there

THIS CASE AD of 1895 illustrates the close kinship of steam engines and threshing machines as king and queen of the machinery world. Nearly every company strove to manufacture and market both together. However many threshermen would swear by one make of engine and another make of threshing machine, thereby "mixing breeds" to their own satisfaction.

developed a parallel interest in road locomotives, as they were called. Even after the advent of railroads there was a great need for moving freight over country roads or across prairies, especially in the west which was now opening up for large scale production of grains, lumber and mining. Road locomotives, or steam wagons as they were sometimes called, were merely traction engines with wheels suited to road travel. England had gone in for them first, and the American picked up where the British left off. American steam wagons were built and tried out in most parts of the country. One turned up in Minnesota in 1860 with 12-foot diameter wheels which traveled two miles per hour and hauled 20 tons of freight on a string of wagons. These steam wagon trains were most used in Nebraska, Colorado, and California where they were employed largely to haul wheat to rail heads, as well as to carry equipment and supplies to isolated mining towns.

The road locomotives did make enough headway to scare the railroads into getting out branch lines to remote places, but they were never an important factor in American transportation.

Self-propelled engines working in fields pulling plows and other equipment were dogged by traction problems. Virtually all the early behemoths that demonstrated for groups of curious farmers were open to the criticism of getting bogged down in soft farm fields. There were two ways to get around this drawback, short of cutting back drastically on the size of the engines, which the early manufacturers were loath to do. Engineers dealt with traction difficulties either by making the drivewheels bigger and broader, or by experimenting with the crawler principle. The huge plowing and threshing engines used on the Great Plains and Far West had enormous wheels, some with extensions as wide as 20 feet. This made them hard to maneuver and practical only in wide open country. It contributed also to their early demise.

The crawler principle, using drums, planks, belts, and even balls, was tried out in the very beginning of steam tractor history. Tracks were used on the Fawkes steam plow, but the engineering of the time was not up to the job of making them practicable and maneuverable.

Thomas S. Minnis of Pennsylvania patented in 1870 a steam tractor that moved on three tracks, two in the rear and one in front, with the two rear tracks operated by different engines. He brought the Minnis Crawler to Ames, Iowa, to demonstrate it on Iowa soils.

The Parvin steam tractor, one of the earliest built in Illinois, moved on an endless chain of steel plates shod with pieces of two-inch plank.

California manufacturers Daniel Best and Benjamin Holt are usually credited with developing the crawler, probably because they founded companies that were the antecedents of the Caterpillar tractors of modern times. Best first built a monstrous big-wheel outfit with two wood-covered drive wheels 15 feet wide and nine feet high. This engine weighed more than 40 tons. Holt took the wheels of a big conventional steam tractor and substituted rough wooden tracks. A separate clutch for each track inaugurated the practice of steering by engaging and disengaging clutches. This principle is used on virtually all crawlers today. The Best-Holt experiments came to fruition in the 1890s and just after the turn of the century. Gas tractors were then just coming in, so the most important development of crawlers was shifted to the internal combustion period.

Out West where the reapers and threshers were combined almost from the beginning, farmers were accustomed to large machines. Huge combines drawn by as many as 40 horses were ripe for the substitution of steam power. Dry country was more suitable for big engines because the soil was seldom wet and boggy at harvest time.

A development during the rather brief steam power period in the West might be considered a precursor to the power takeoff which is used so extensively today. While huge combines were hauled along by a steam tractor, some combines were fitted with their own steam engines to handle the power requirements of cutting and threshing. These auxiliary engines were operated from a steam line going to the main traction engine as the source of supply — a sort of power takeoff, vintage 1900. Steam pressure was also used to raise big gang plows from the ground, thus pointing the way for modern hydraulic systems.

From 1870 to 1890 the use of traction engines advanced steadily all over the country. However, their supremacy was overwhelmingly in belt work. Multiple plows pulled by steam tractors were developed rapidly in the 1890s, and many were sold in the open wheat country where plowing was an important function of the engines. By 1900 there were 30 firms in the United States building 5,000 large engines a year for use in the United States and Canada. The biggest engines (up to 120 horsepower) went West, while the small and moderate size engines, 15 to 35 horsepower, remained in the East and Middle West. There were horizontal tube boilers and vertical tube boilers operating under pressures of 100 to 200 pounds per square inch. Most

common was the horizontal boiler which could also serve as the frame of the engine. The firebox was at the rear and supplied partial support for the big traction wheels. Since engines had to travel over all kinds of rough terrain, the problem of cushioning the main boiler assembly from the hazards of the road was met by using very heavy coil springs with varied mounting arrangements.

The engine parts were attached to the boiler at various locations, both under and over. Flues had varying arrangements with a view to increasing efficiency. The smokestack might be either at the front or the rear. In either case a screen bonnet usually capped the stack to squelch the sparks which were the bane of steam engine operation in dry areas.

In some parts of the country water quality was a constant headache. Boiler parts caked and clogged with lime and other sediment were a constant hazard to both efficiency and safety. Most states set up official steam engine inspec-

THE WHEAT GROWING plains of Manitoba and Saskatchewan used big threshing rigs and furnished machinery manufacturers with one of their best markets. The sheer size of machines and the crews required to operate them was one of the reasons for their decline, however. These pictures, loaned by Professor Clarence Clausen of St. Olaf College, were taken of the Clausen-Lokness rig and crew at Govan, Saskatchewan, in 1913. The crew consisted of ten teamsters, two field pitchers, two spike pitchers, two water "monkeys", one engineer, one separator man, and one straw "monkey". There were also two women cooks.

THE REALLY BIG steam machines had their development in California, where engine style was more or less separate from the rest of the nation. Two manufacturers, Daniel Best and Benjamin Holt, founded separate lines. They and other family members were bitter rivals but eventually merged. The engine shown below is a Best machine, featuring the huge drums that were used as drive wheels on the first steamers. These unbelievably big and clumsy rigs took the place of the massive horse-drawn combines that had utilized teams of 20 to 40 horses and mules.

tion services and licensing procedures to guard against careless use which might lead to explosions. Manufacturers devised many kinds of safety valves and fitted their boilers with replaceable soft metal plugs to quiet the fears of farmers. Safety was always an important advertising point.

Since steam engine operation usually peaked in fall when both threshing and plowing were at their height, freezing was a hazard to both boilers and tanks.

Efficiency and greater horsepower were achieved through scores of improvements such as better balance, higher piston speed with shorter stroke, compound cylinder action, valves with closer tolerances, and many other engineering changes. Average horse-

power grew from around 10 in 1875 to around 40 in 1910.

Of course there were some bigger engines. The plains states had a hearty appetite for bigness. Forty or 50 horsepower was, however, the practical limit on big engines. Gaar-Scott marketed around 1910 a Big Forty which carried 21 barrels of water when plowing and weighed when loaded 35,000 pounds. This engine had two tandem-compound cylinders. Case built the biggest steam tractor, intended for hauling, plowing, and belt work. Fully loaded with fuel and water, it weighed 46,000 pounds, delivered better than 200 horsepower at the belt, pulled 24 14-inch plows, or 50 tons of freight in wagons. These engines exceed-

ed the limit of practicability, and few were built.

It is of interest that one engine was built with four-wheel drive by Wood, Taber and Morse, one of the oldest of the eastern machinery companies. The steering of this engine was too clumsy and the extra gearing, always a headache on big engines, doomed this experiment to failure.

Case was one of the first and by long odds the greatest builder of American steam engines. The company started (except for a few experimental models) in 1875 with 75 engines. Building in all sizes, the company peaked in 1911 with 2321 engines. It stopped making steam engines in 1924 in which year only 130 went on the market.

In all 35,737 machines were built by Case. Geiser was second with 15,801, and Huber third with 11,568. (These statistics are from Wik's *Steam Power on the American Farm*, secured originally from company records.)

As gas tractors began to take over from 1910 on, steam engine demand moved westward, north into Canada, and into grain production areas abroad. Indeed, at one time the exports of steam engines by American companies were considerable. In 1899 Case sold 25 complete threshing rigs in South America, mostly in the Argentine. Gaar-Scott and Huber sold quite a few machines in Europe, notably in Russia, Sweden, and Denmark. British exports

THE CRAWLER PRINCIPLE of locomotion had been tried repeatedly in both England and the United States in an effort to make heavy engines practical for use on soft farmland. However, it remained for Benjamin Holt to come up with a practical crawler in 1906. Both the Best and Holt companies are considered antecedants of the Caterpillar Tractor Company which eventually established its headquarters at Peoria, Illinois. The first crawlers were steered by a wheel, or a pair of wheels in front, but later steering was accomplished by having a clutch for each set of tracks, thereby permitting the large machines to pivot sharply.

to Canada dropped off sharply as American machines just across the border found a ready market. Britain did most of its business in its colonies and in Australia.

Fortunately for steam buffs, the steam engine boom on American farms has become the best publicized and most demonstrated phase of farm mechanization. Steam engines and threshing operations have caught the national interest. Many engines were still in pretty good condition when they were displaced by internal combustion tractors. Somehow they escaped the scrap iron drives of two world wars. They were ready to be rebuilt and refurbished along about 1940 when the rage for steam threshing reunions seized the alumni of the steam era. One of the oldest and most successful among a hundred or more of steam threshing shows held in all parts of this country and Canada was established at Mt. Pleasant, Iowa. It started as a one-day event, increased to five days, and eventually became a kind of continuous museum show with demonstrations and events running throughout the year. It is not necessary, however, to travel a long distance to see a steam show. Look around and you will undoubtedly find one nearby. If you see a field of old-fashioned grain shocks in July or August, chances are it is grain being readied for a threshing show.

The shows have branched out to include other operations besides threshing, and more recently they have been extended to preserving the amazing variety of gas tractors which began coming out around 1910, and had the steamers pretty well shoved off the map by 1925.

Steam had its drawbacks which could not be overcome by sentiment and romance. In the first quarter of the 1900s petroleum fuels were dirt cheap, 10 cents a gallon or less. Internal combustion engines were practical in smaller sizes than steam engines. In the end they required more careful engineering, but that precision engineering was forthcoming. American farmers intensified their mechanization kick as the 1900s got under way.

Steam was never able to unseat the horses, but the small gas tractor was in the wings, ready to do what steam never succeeded in doing.

Color Illustrations

WINDMILLS deserve top billing in any publication about farm power which looks to the past with an eye on the future. They may have a more important place on the farm as a result of the wide search for sources of power that do not depend so heavily on fossil fuels. Although they have served farmers for well over 100 years, most intensively in the late 1800s, they have never received the attention they deserve from the engineering fraternity. This illustration of a comparatively modern windmill is from a catalog of Flint and Walling Manufacturing Company of Kendalville, Indiana.

PERHAPS THE BEST known advertising emblem in the entire history of farm machinery was the Case Eagle, originally called Old Abe. Case has had a part in farm machinery development since before the Civil War, having had a hand in practically every facet of mechanization, beginning with the early Groundhog-type threshing machine.

Established 1842

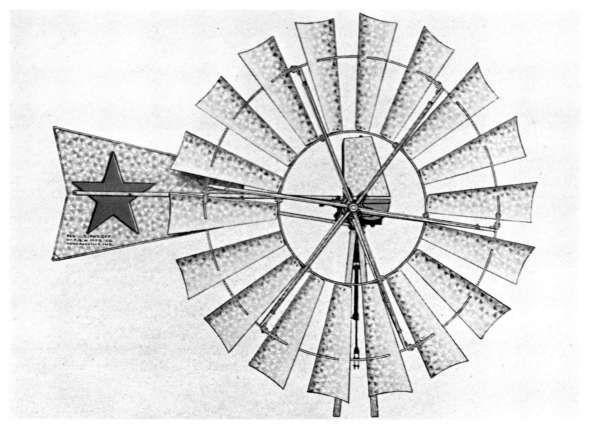

65

FARMERS HAVE ALWAYS been fascinated by trials and demonstrations of the latest in machinery. Prairie Farmer started sponsoring machinery shows as early as 1870 and at present sponsors the largest of them all, along with its sister publications, Wallaces Farmer and Wisconsin Agriculturist. Here are scenes from the Farm Progress Show, held the last week in September every year in either Indiana, Iowa, or Illinois. This demonstration now sets the pace for the entire country in farm mechanization.

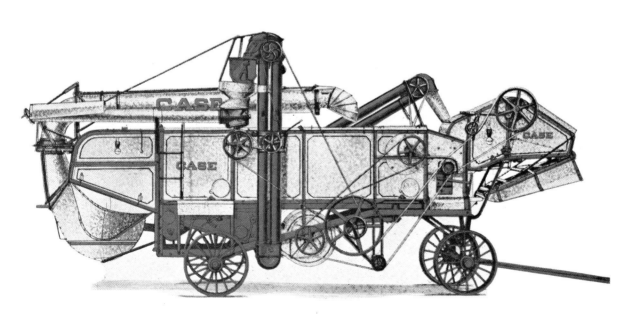

67

STEAM POWER is responsible for the most romantic period in the whole history of farm mechanization. There are in this country and Canada literally scores of steam threshing shows that each year draw thousands of steam engine buffs and others eager to get a glimpse of the exciting period of the itinerant threshing rig. One of the oldest and probably the biggest of these "reunions" is the one held each year at Mt. Pleasant, Iowa. In recent years this has grown into a perpetual museum and performance center celebrating the great days of steam. These pictures are used by courtesy of the Mt. Pleasant organization.

"the greatest STEAM show on earth"

68

Photos courtesy of the Old Settlers & Threshers Association Inc., Mount Pleasant, Iowa.

COLORFUL catalogs touting the prowess of steam engines and gas tractors are among the rarest items at antique shows these days. Competition in the farm power field was terrific, from the early days of the field harvester down to the present. At left is the engine that couldn't make up its mind. The Townsend Company of Janesville, Wisconsin, caught between steam and gas, put a gas engine on top of a steam chassis, using the entire boiler as a radiator. BELOW is part of the back page of a Russell catalog. Russell was one of the oldest names in the business, involved in both steam and gas tractors and other farm machinery.

The Unexcelled RUSSELL Products

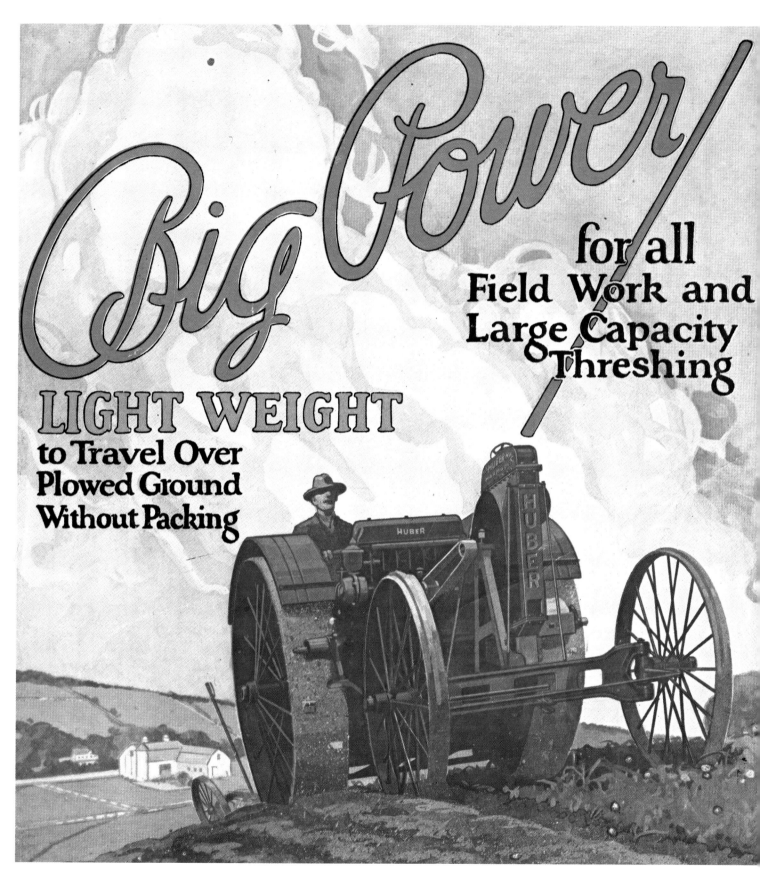

America's Oldest Farm Paper

THE PRAIRIE FARMER

Founded In 1841

Seventy-fifth Year   JULY 31, 1915   *Every Other Saturday*

Come to the World's Greatest Tractor Demonstration, Champaign, Illinois, August 3-4-5-6

GAS-OIL TRACTORS

Mechanization triumphant!

FIELD TRIALS of farm machinery have been a favorite activity of farmers for more than 100 years. Interest in gas tractors was no exception. Here is a Prairie Farmer front page plugging one of the biggest of demonstrations held back in August, 1915. Both large and small tractors were shown. The small ones were just beginning to edge out the monsters that had been built on steam engine lines.

Steam power for farming reached its peak of usefulness, perhaps even its peak of mechanical engineering, in 1910. Gas tractors, oil tractors, internal combustion tractors — whatever you want to call them — were getting ready to take over. Today, when we face high cost and possible exhaustion of petroleum products, we may think it too bad that further refinement of steam power was passed over at the time, but the picture was different just before World War I. Oil wells were beginning to gush, lubricating oils were improving fast, gasoline and kerosene were dirt cheap.

The great tide of immigration which assured cheap labor was tapering off. From the time of the Gold Rush and the Civil War, American farmers had been loath to pay out money for hired help. They acquired a taste for labor saving machines early in our history.

Useful as it was for furnishing belt power, the steam engine had always required a good deal of manpower to attend its needs. When it became evident that one man on a big gas tractor could do what two or three could do with a steam engine, the handwriting was on the wall.

Throughout the history of American agriculture, an over-riding goal has been to save man-hours and extend productivity.

Steam tractors had from the beginning been too heavy and clumsy. A weight of 500 to 700 pounds per drawbar horsepower was too much to lug around. It took a great deal of power to move the power plant and did not leave enough for useful work. Fuel to make steam was cheap, but water was often hard to come by. It took something like 20 barrels a day to keep a big steamer going in the field.

It has been said that the Winnipeg plowing matches of 1910 started a decisive trend against steam. On that occasion fields were soaked by heavy rains. The massive steam engines quickly mired down, and gas tractors were used to pull them out. This occurred in spite of the fact that the first gas tractors were themselves bedeviled by too much weight per horsepower. Smaller gas tractors were now being built. The boom years of World War I, even before the United States got into the fighting, placed a premium on farm production. Farmers were prosperous, short of help, and ready to pour big money into a great spurt of mechanization.

However, steam power did not fade away immediately. It remained the power of choice for

THE FIRST experimental self-propelled gas tractors came out during the 1890s. The first exclusively tractor factory was established in Charles City, Iowa, by the firm of Hart-Parr in 1901. The Hart-Parr No. 1, shown at top, is often called the first practical gas tractor. It was built in 1901, sold to an Iowa farmer in 1902, and is said to have operated for 17 years. Just below it is No. 2, built in 1903. This one had two horizontal cylinders and was cooled by oil.

HENRY FORD had an itch to get into the tractor business but did not consider himself ready until 1915 when he started building the Fordson. Shown here is an experimental model with a Ford car engine and binder bullwheels. The Fordson was unveiled in 1917.

threshing, lumber sawing and some other belt power jobs. Engineers hated to abandon entirely the steam engine with its quiet, vibrationless power, capable of handling overloads more effectively than its gasoline powered successor.

Gas engines brought their own set of irritations. The massive one- and two-lungers that inaugurated the petroleum age were desperately hard to start, their exhausts blasted out like cannon, and their massive flywheels restored much of the weight that had been spared by the elimination of steam boilers. Passing of steam power relieved the farmer of the fear of explosion and the annoyances of boiler scale and engineer licenses, but replaced these drawbacks with a new set of challenges that could be just as annoying. However, gas engines fascinated the younger farmers of that day. Steam was not for everyone, but the gas engine and tractor could be used profitably on even small farms. Thus was born the farm boy mechanic who could take anything apart and put it together again.

The Model T and other early cars had whetted the appetite for "monkeying" with engines. The tractor was right in line for the same kind of attention. Fortunately, the motors of that day were relatively simple. Nevertheless they often displayed an orneriness that matched the most stubborn critters of the mule skinner era.

In 1910 most older farmers still preferred the mule and the horse. The steam engine had done very little to unseat horse power in its original form. Steam was never adapted to the lesser tasks of the medium-size farm. On the other hand, the small gas tractor could do almost anything a horse could do, and do it on cheap gas instead of oats and hay. The tractor could even be hitched to horse-drawn machinery, which made the transition easier.

Even so, the gas tractor did not actually put the horse out of business until around 1930. From World War I on, the eventual outcome was never in doubt. The horse was doomed as a source of farm power, much to the dismay of many farmers who loved horses and who were fond of saying that the exhaust of a horse was good for the land while the exhaust of a tractor was so much waste.

As a boy on the farm, the author experienced the transition first hand. Many a father, determined to stick with horse farming, was overruled by his boys who took to tinkering with engines as ducks take to water. Reluctant fathers finally admitted grudgingly that the man with a tractor got his work done ahead of the farmer with horses. And that was that!

The development of the gas tractor was more rapid than the growth of steam power for several reasons. It was carried along by the increasing momentum of the automobile. The prosperity of World War I served as a stimulus to farmers with small and medium size holdings. Perhaps most important of all was the acceleration of the mechanical age on all fronts.

Inventors started experimenting with what they called explosion engines nearly two centuries before these became a really important factor in furnishing power for an industrial age. It was logical that gunpowder should be the first fuel and that somehow the cylinder should be equated with the barrel of a cannon. This occurred as early as 1678 in France. (Engine buffs will recall that as late as the year 1900 gun cartridges were used to start the massive single cylinder engines on the first oil tractors.)

Early progress on gas engines was painfully slow. Pioneering was done by the French, the Ger

JOHN FROELICH started building experimental tractors as early as 1892. At top is one of his first models. It was the forerunner of the Waterloo Boy line which later became the foundation for John Deere tractors. Just above is shown the 1906 International built for International Harvester by the Ohio Manufacturing Company of Upper Sandusky, Ohio.

75

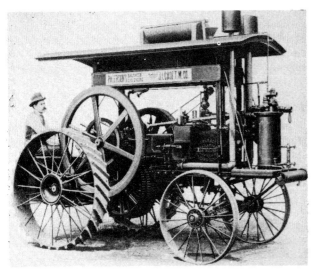

ON THIS PAGE are three old timers from the 1890s. Top illustration is a Patterson from the middle of the decade which headed the Case line to come later. Center is an Otto tractor from Philadelphia which found its way out to North Dakota. Lower picture is a Flour City from 1899, made by Kinnard in Minneapolis.

mans, and the British. Explosion engines were first designed for limited purposes, sometimes requiring only one stroke of the piston. The action of a piston working in a cylinder was relatively simple, but ignition and carburetion were much more serious obstacles. Coal gas, coal dust, turpentine, and paraffin were among the early fuels. Ignition was accomplished by open flame devices, heated tubes, and finally in the 1880s crude applications of electricity. The modern sparkplug with its attendant timer or distributor was not perfected until around 1900. Before that a number of kinds of breaker devices were used to create a properly timed spark.

Both the two- and four-cycle (stroke) principles were used on early engines. Enormous flywheels, some weighing a ton or more, were needed to carry the big pistons over compression points. As with steam, the first engines were stationary. It was not until the last years of the 1800s that serious thought was given to making oil engines self-propelled.

The progress of internal combustion motors before the year 1890 was seriously hampered by two situations. One was the slow development of petroleum fuels and lubricating oils. The proliferation of products made from petroleum is a comparatively recent development. Older people living today can easily remember when kerosene was the principal petroleum product. It was called coal oil and used primarily for kerosene lamps and household oil stoves employed for cooking in summer. At the turn of the century gasoline was relatively unimportant, considered too explosive to bother with. The various grades of cruder distillates that we lump today under the name of fuel oil or diesel fuel were not widely made or used.

That is undoubtedly why the earliest tractors burned kerosene, using gasoline only for starting, or an evil smelling fluid called carbon disulfide. High compression engines burning high test gas did not come on the market until the 1930s.

Serviceable lubricating oils capable of standing the heat generated by explosion engines also were hard to come by. Almost any kind of oil could be used to lubricate a steam engine. In fact, animal and vegetable oils of all kinds were pressed into service. These left objectionable residues when subjected to the intense heat of an internal combustion engine. The fact that early gas engine operators were looking hard for really good cylinder oil is attested to by the vigorous advertising of brand name oils in farm papers around 1900.

TOP PICTURE is a Dissinger from the year 1904, made in Philadelphia. Just above is a picture (courtesy of the Western Development Museum in Canada) of the Hovland Traveling Thresher, made in Minneapolis and South Dakota by August Hovland who had a hand in designing the whole unit, windrower, tractor, and threshing machine. The fact that it was one of the first successful windrowers may have had much to do with its popularity in Canada where it got more attention than in the United States.

BELOW is a really big gas tractor plowing in North Dakota. The first tractors were handicapped by the fact that they were built on the specifications of the big steam engines, often being mounted on frames and wheels used by steamers.

First Best Tracklayer—the '75

Another deterrent to development of the gas engine was the curious fact of basic patents being held by one not-very-progressive company. The Otto Company of Philadelphia produced the first practical four-cycle engine around 1876 and was able to protect it with patents until 1890 when the lid blew off and invention began to hum on all fronts. The Otto Company did succeed in building one of the first self-propelled tractors, but never became important in the tractor market.

It is a bit surprising to note that, both in England and America, patent laws were enacted early and were quite effective. Sophisticated schemes for getting around patents and buying and selling franchises came about later.

After 1890 things began to stir in the gas tractor field. By the year 1910 there were only about 1000 petroleum burning tractors in the whole country. However, that year was the turning point and the beginning of the production explosion.

In the year 1912, 12,000 tractors were built. The advent of the smaller tractor for the family farm and the feverish demand for food during World War I were the signals for everybody to get into the business. Britain alone ordered 6,000 tractors in the United States during the war years, indicating that development here was progressing more rapidly than in Europe.

At first only large companies, most of them manufacturers of steam tractors, decided that this was the shape of the future. By 1912, not only the steam engine companies, but scores of others including the budding automobile makers got into the act. As with the automobile, tractors sprouted in all sorts of small town and country machine shops.

AT RIGHT is an American tractor which won a silver medal at the Winnipeg trials in 1909, the year that the swing from steam to gasoline began to reach full momentum.

OPPOSITE PAGE shows tractors of the Best and Holt lines around the year 1910. Eventually these were merged into the Caterpillar Company and the headquarters moved to Peoria, Illinois. The Holt name persisted for some time after the move. The lower machine shows the Caterpillar trademark used for the first time. The illustration at the bottom on this page shows a Holt combine, with a crawler tractor in the shape it finally assumed.

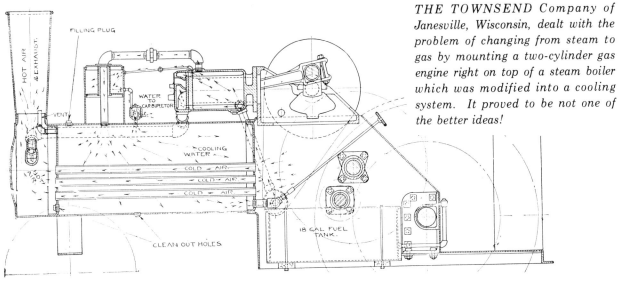

THE TOWNSEND Company of Janesville, Wisconsin, dealt with the problem of changing from steam to gas by mounting a two-cylinder gas engine right on top of a steam boiler which was modified into a cooling system. It proved to be not one of the better ideas!

THREE-WHEELERS in various arrangements started off the small tractor rage in the years 1914 and 1915. The "Bull with a pull" shown in the top illustration was one of the most popular. This 1913 model delivered 5-12 horsepower, had a two-cylinder engine. Two years later the company, based in Minneapolis, built a bigger one. The machine at left is a Trenam 12-24 made in Wisconsin.

The slowest period of gas tractor design and manufacture came when the machines were merely an adaptation of the self-propelled steamer. They were big and clumsy and good mostly for belt power. In fact, the first gas tractors were engines mounted on steam engine frames and wheels. With steam the business end, or actual engine, was relatively small and light. The gas motor had to be much larger, consisting in early stages of one or two massive cylinders and two even more massive flywheels.

Radiators were also large. Attempts to cool with oil were abandoned in favor of water in quantity, 50 to 100 gallons or even more. One manufacturer of steam engines, Townsend, merely mounted the gas engine on top of the boiler and used the entire boiler capacity for cooling. The result was a tractor almost indistinguishable from a steam engine, using the boiler both as a frame and a radiator.

The early tractors used big tanks for cooling. Even when the modern radiator principle of many finned ducts was adopted, there was no circulating pump. Water in quantity was essential, and the sheer volume precluded any possibility of using an anti-freeze solution.

A massive single cylinder with a waterjacket and cooling system was the heart of the first oil tractors. The exhaust could be heard over in the next county. In those days there were no government regulations forbidding ear-splitting sounds. Usually these one-lungers had two huge flywheels to maintain momentum between firings of the cylinder. By 1912

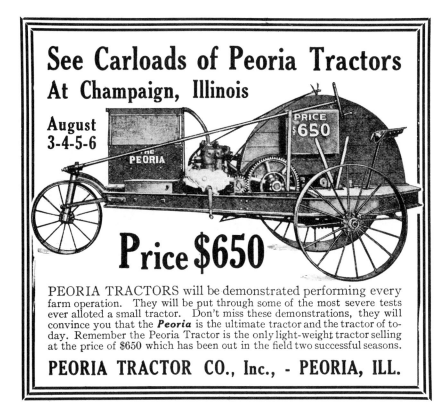

HORSES *successfully resisted the steam age. In the year 1910 they still had 20 years of strong competition against tractors ahead of them. Manufacturers of small tractors, attempting a takeover, tried to build machines that could be hitched successfully to horse-drawn equipment. They even tried to fool farmers into thinking that they were driving horses. Leather lines for remote control and other devices which permitted the farmer to ride the working implement rather than the tractor were considered ways to convert skeptical farmers.*

MINNEAPOLIS Steel and Machinery Company which made the Twin City line of tractors was slow to join the big stampede to small machines. They undoubtedly had their eyes on the threshing and plowing trade in the Dakotas and Canada which still called for large tractors. In 1915 even Twin City broke with tradition and featured a small "15" for the 160-acre farm. It had a four-cylinder engine, four wheels, and avoided the two- and three-wheel types that were popular for a time. The advertisement boasts that this little tractor can handle a 24-inch separator.

most manufacturers had shifted to two cylinders, positioned horizontally either side by side or opposed, thereby making it possible to reduce the size of the flywheels. Around 1915 tractor people followed the automobile manufacturers by going to four vertical cylinders.

It is likely that the first self-propelled gas tractors in the United States were six machines built by the Charter Gas Engine Company which in 1889 put their single cylinder engine on a Rumley steam tractor chassis. A more workable machine was put together in 1892 by John Froelich of Iowa who mounted a Van Duzen gas engine on a Robinson running gear with traction gearing of his own invention. The most notable thing about his accomplishment was that his tractor eventually became the Waterloo Boy and therefore the forerunner of the whole John Deere line.

The Case Threshing Machine Company built an experimental tractor the same year, 1892, using an engine designed by William Patterson. By 1895 they had a two-cylinder opposed engine which they used in their larger tractors until 1912. Case Company was always cautious, however, and took its time about getting gas tractors on the market.

The International Harvester Company, which had stayed away from steam engines, was one of the early birds in the gas field. The McCormick Company had built a gas engine in 1897 and put it on wheels the next year. It was a two-cylinder opposed engine not unlike the Case except that it used a friction transmission. However, International waited until 1905 to start its permanent line when it purchased several Morton tractors manufactured for it by the Ohio Manufacturing Company.

A number of other tractors were launched in the 1890s, the Sterling, the Otto, the Lambert, the Huber, and the Flour City (Kinnard-Haines).

Immediately after the turn of the century appeared what was for a time the most famous name in gas tractors, the Hart-Parr. C. W. Hart and C. H. Parr started experimenting with building a tractor in the late 1890s. In 1903 they established the first tractor factory at Charles City, Iowa. Most manufacturers of the time had well developed lines of other farm machinery, including steam engines, but Hart-Parr was exclusively a gas tractor factory. It was credited with producing the first line of really practical tractors. Their Old Reliable, a 30-60, built in 1907, threshed for an Iowa farmer for nearly 20 years before it was retired. In that year it is estimated that of the 600 tractors in use in the United States and Canada one-third were Hart-Parrs. This company is also credited with in-

venting the word "tractor." Up to that time the accepted description had been "gasoline traction engine."

Henry Ford, who was already building his Ford empire at this time, based on the assembly line manufacturing method, had an itch to get into the tractor business. His experiments in this field started around 1900, and resulted in some rather large experimental models. In 1907 he built a tractor based on the engine of the Model T and the bull wheels from a binder. This may have given him the idea for the Fordson for the small farm which was launched with much fanfare in 1915.

In spite of the growing interest in gas tractors and the appearance of some new companies from 1900 on, the steam engine manufacturers pretty much dominated the gas tractor field until 1912. They unfortunately brought with them some of the clumsy designs of the

TRACTORS on this page date back to 1915. Some tricycle types had the third wheel in front, some in back. Most tried to get the farmer as close to his tillage machine as possible, preferably right on top!

For Pleasure and Profit

The Utility Tractor

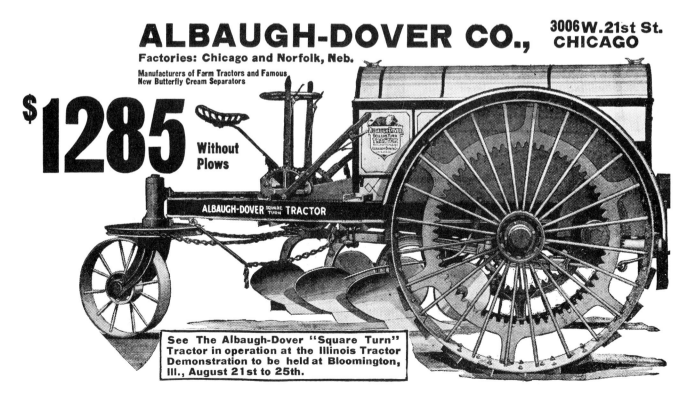

steam age. The firms that built gas tractors along with their steam lines include Case, Buffalo Pitts, Gaar-Scott, Aultman-Taylor, Minneapolis, Rumley, Avery, and Reeves. Some established gas tractor lines that replaced their steam engines; others faded quickly.

By 1912 these and other companies had flooded the markets in the United States and Canada with big tractors. That year alone 12,000 were built in spite of the fact that farmers were becoming disillusioned with the hard-starting, ponderous brutes that, like the steam tractors, were only suited for belt work and plowing on very large farms. Old tractors were abandoned in tractor graveyards and sometimes right in the fields where they had steadfastly refused to start. It was said that tractor manufacturers had more mechanics running around starting engines than they had salesmen, and that was not a formula for success.

Then the inevitable happened. Spurred on by the agricultural prosperity of the war years, the companies started to make small tractors that could be used on ordinary farms and that could be attached to horse-drawn machinery. These tractors handled two or three plow bottoms, no more. True, the threshing machines had to be reduced in size so they could be handled by a farm tractor. Other belt jobs on the farm, silo filling, feed grinding, corn shredding and shelling, and the like, could be handled very well with the small tractor which had a higher RPM and a smaller pulley size than the big brutes.

Simultaneously with the reduction in size came a number of innovative changes. There was a premium on four cylinder engines of the type that were powering automobiles of the time. There was a flurry of structural changes calculated to make the farm tractor just as useful as the horse. There were many two- and three-wheelers as well as different arrangements of the conventional four wheels. To secure traction on a light machine, deep cutting lugs were attached to the traction wheels. There were also rather bizarre efforts to design drive wheels to run in furrows, and front end self-steering devices. The wildest scheme of all was to drive the tractor with leather lines from a wagon or horse-type tillage implement. The idea of interchangeable plows and other implements for a single power plant also had its origin at that time.

Traction was always a problem with a light tractor, so it is not surprising that quite a few small track type tractors were put on

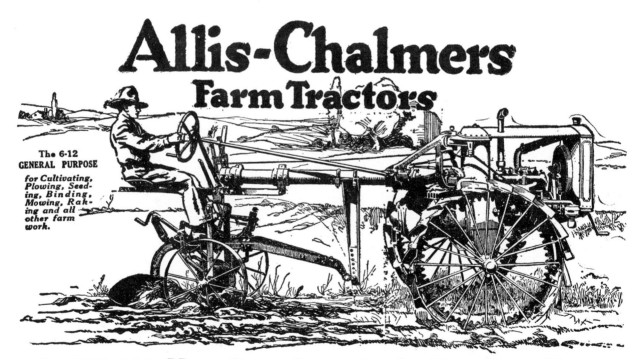

ONE MAN CAN FARM MORE LAND *with the*

Plowing

Harrowing

Seeding

Cultivating

Mowing

MOLINE
UNIVERSAL TRACTOR
"It Solves the Farm Help Problem"

TWO MILLION MEN will be gone from the farms because of the war —strong, skilled, willing workers, only a small part of whom can be replaced by older men, boys and women. Yet production of food must be increased. There is only one way—equip the men left on the farms so they can do more work than ever before.

With the Moline-Universal—the original two-wheel tractor—*One Man* can farm more land than was ever before possible, because—

One Man has power at his command equal to five horses, capable of doing the work of seven horses owing to its greater speed and endurance. This power is always available for any farm work.

One Man operates the Moline-Universal Tractor from the seat of the implement to which it is attached, where he must sit in order to do good work.

One Man can start in the spring and go from one operation to another—plowing, harrowing, planting, cultivating, mowing, harvesting grain or corn, spreading manure, filling the silo, cutting wood, etc., doing all farm work from one year's end to another, independently of horses or hired help.

All these one-man operations with the Moline-Universal are possible because it is mounted on two wheels, all its weight is traction weight; it is powerful—pulls two 14-inch bottoms easily—yet it is light so that it does not pack the soil. The Moline-Universal attaches direct to the implement, making one compact unit.

One woman or boy operates the Moline-Universal as easily as a man. Miss Ruth Harding of Albion, N. Y., a proud owner of a Moline-Universal, writes: "I have never called a man from his work to assist me with the tractor in any way."

Thousands of Moline-Universal Tractors are now at work under every conceivable condition in all parts of the United States and in Canada, England, France, Sweden, Norway, Denmark, Russia, Italy, Spain, Mexico, Peru, Argentine, Brazil, Cuba, Gautemala, South Africa, Australia. Wherever a Moline-Universal Tractor is sold there is immediately a big demand for more.

The demand for Moline-Universal Tractors has far exceeded our expectations. We built an enormous factory which is devoted entirely to making Moline-Universal Tractors and three times have erected large additions to cope with the enormous demand. We now have the largest tractor factory in the world.

Moline sales and service branches cover the country. No purchaser is ever more than a few hours away from Moline service.

The Moline-Universal will solve your help and power problems. It is ready for you now. Write us today for free booklet giving full description of the Moline-Universal and name of nearest Moline dealer.

Address Department 14

MOLINE PLOW COMPANY, Moline, Illinois

the market. Some followed the crawler principle that had been developed by the Holt Company of California (later of Peoria, Illinois). Others had their own arrangements of drums or tracks for getting a toe hold in the ground without resorting to weight. These were undoubtedly a reaction to the idea that the big tractors packed the soil and diminished the productivity of the land. Nearly every farmer had before him the vision of sterile soil in the path of a big threshing rig that had crossed his field.

In 1913 the Bull Traction Company of Minneapolis designed a light tractor with three wheels and a small four cylinder, 12 horsepower, high speed engine. "The Bull with a pull" is credited by many with starting the rush of small tractors. By 1915 the Bull had zoomed to the top in tractor units put on the market. The company folded by 1918, indicating that there may have been some serious faults in design.

Henry Ford really got into the small tractor act in 1917 after a number of years of experimenting with larger machines which were not seriously marketed. The Fordson was a sensation. It worked in the field at a speed well above the walk of a brisk horse. In high gear

TRACTOR VARIATIONS seem to have been endless during the innovative years of World War I. The Hackney (upper left) was turned out by a St. Paul company in 1912. The name of the game was to outmaneuver the horse. The Square Turn tractor was produced by a Chicago company. Almost simultaneously Minneapolis came up with the Short Turn tractor, shown at right, manufactured by a small company of that name. Needless to say, most of these small companies failed to survive.

on the road it literally flew — by standards of the time, of course.

The fast Fordson with its prominent steel lugs on steel wheels was a "rough riding son-of-a-gun," and rather dangerous. On quick starts anchored to a heavy load, it was known to rear up and flip over on its back, killing or maiming the driver. This danger was averted in subsequent models by changing the hitch, but the tractor got a reputation as the high flyer among farm machines. The engine burned kerosene after a gasoline start and was in most ways a larger replica of the Model T, even to the magneto, spark coils, and timer. The three speed and reverse transmission was of course a departure. Ford established the principle of using the engine itself as a frame and thus simplified construction in many ways.

A number of tractors copied the Ford in several respects, notably the Samson. Case came out with a three-wheeler with the bull wheel running in the furrow and a second traction wheel which could be disengaged by hand to facilitate sharp turns. Moline produced a two-wheeler with traction on both wheels which could be attached to different implements. It permitted the driver to sit on the cultivator or plow, handling the tractor by "remote control."

There was a swarm of other oddball types, all calculated to make the horse farmer feel right at home. Many are illustrated in this volume. Most had in-line four cylinder engines, making it easier and cheaper to put the belt pulley in the front of the tractor on the main shaft. This brought forth some problems in lining up the machine for belt work and necessitated a very small drive pulley. At that time it was deemed necessary to have a pulley on all tractors. The power takeoff method of transmitting power was still some years away.

Crawler tractors, or their equivalent, were well represented among the small tractors that poured onto the market between 1910 and 1920. These included the Bullock Creeper (Chicago 1910), The Yuba (Holt in California 1912), Killen-Strait (Appleton, Wisconsin 1916), Bates Steel Mule (Joliet, Illinois 1916), Trundaar (Anderson, Indiana 1916), Bear (New York 1918), and the Cleveland-Cletrac (1918). This is not a complete list.

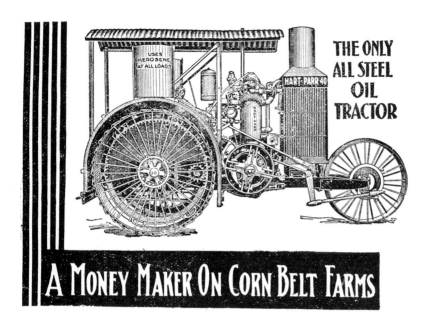

Made World War I tanks

The greatest impact of World War I on the development of tractors was in supplying a hot market for small tractors on farms. However, a few companies turned to making military equipment, notably Holt-Caterpillar and Hart-Parr. Some of the most important patents in crawler improvement were developed by Holt-Caterpillar in producing the military tank and various types of tractor crawlers for army use.

The older and more conservative manufacturers refused to join the mad rush into odd-ball types during this era of rapid tractor expansion. They continued to make big machines and added some medium sized models to meet the demand from the general farm trade. Except for its one excursion into a three-wheel model, not notably successful, Case changed its two-cylinder opposed tractor into a four cylinder line with conventional wheels, making it in several sizes.

International produced first its small single cylinder Mogul and then its 15-30 Titan, a three-bottom tractor with chain drive which became a fixture on farms that needed a medium-size power plant. They then went to the conventional four wheel McCormick-Deering which also did well. Their first radical change came in 1924 when the company came out with the row-crop Farmall line. This tricycle type, intended primarily for cultivating corn and powered for two plow bottoms, was the radical innovation of the 1920s. Practically all companies eventually copied the Farmall in one shape or another, except Ford who steadfastly refused to change his Fordson.

John Deere built its tractor line on a foundation which had been laid by John Froelich in 1893 when he organized the Waterloo Gas Traction Engine Company. The Waterloo series was stabilized in 1916 by the unveiling of the John Deere Waterloo Boy, a two cylinder, side by side, horizontal kerosene burning engine with a 180-degree crankshaft. Thus was born the "tut-tut, tut-tut" engine which was music on American farms for nearly 30 years. This economical, vibration free (due to the unusual firing rhythm) engine was one of the wonders of the tractor world. John Deere abandoned it with great reluctance long after other firms had gone to vertical fours and sixes. Deere made it in several sizes and used it effectively in all its row-crop tractors as well as four wheel models. Tractor models come and go, but the old John Deere "tut-tut, tut-tut" seems to go on forever. There are thousands still in use.

The growth of the tractor business during the years of World War I was to say the least fantastic. By 1917 the market had grown to 90,000 and by 1920 to 200,000, a fourth of them Fordsons.

Big tractors were also being built during those years by the older companies to meet the need for replacement of steam engines for threshing. However, after the big tractor glut of 1912, manufacturers were cautious and took their time about engineering changes. During the years when the spotlight was entirely on the small tractors, some very excellent lines of large and medium-size tractors were quietly developed by Avery, Rumley, Aultman-Taylor, International, Case, Oliver, Hart-Parr, Massey-Harris, Allis-Chalmers, Minneapolis-Moline, and others.

HART-PARR of Charles City, Iowa, has been credited with producing the first practical gas tractor. The company started with big machines and began to reduce size when it became evident that the future belonged to the smaller farm tractor. The advertisement just above is from 1912 and featured one of the big engines. On the opposite page are three Hart-Parrs (from the top) 1913, 1914, and 1915, indicating the shift to lower horsepower and greater maneuverability. The Hart-Parr operation was eventually absorbed by Oliver.

La Crosse Happy Farmer TRACTOR

IN three short years, the satisfaction of thousands of owners of Happy Farmer Tractors has built the great business and the 16 big factory buildings of the Happy Farmer Tractor organization. Every man who owns a Happy Farmer Tractor boosts for it. His own experience has shown him that the Happy Farmer is the perfect, one man, kerosene burning tractor for the farm of any size.

From start to finish the Happy Farmer Tractor is built for leadership. Every part of it is made in the Happy Farmer plant by the highest grade workmen and the most up-to-date machinery.

So many thousands of farmers want the Happy Farmer that we cannot keep pace with the demand, although we are continually increasing our manufacturing facilities.

The Right Design

That the Happy Farmer with its wide tread and perfect balance, is the right design of tractor, is proved by its use. Experience has shown that this design delivers more power with less weight.

The Happy Farmer turns in its own tracks to right or left with equal ease.

While it is rated at only 12-24 horsepower, it can always be counted upon to deliver much more than this whenever you need it.

Because the Happy Farmer is so simple and because of our great factory, big buying power, and expert organization, we can offer this master tractor for the low price of $1075.

Happy Farmer Tractor Implements

Happy Farmer Tractor Implements give the same satisfaction as the Happy Farmer Tractor. All Happy Farmer Moldboard Plows are automatically controlled by a cord from the driver's seat on the tractor.

The Happy Farmer Disk Harrow is made especially for tractor work. The Happy Farmer Drill is the only proven successful one with automatic patented power-lift and power pressure.

See The Next Demonstration

Performance in the field is a tractor's only test. Watch the Happy Farmer yourself and you will see why it is America's greatest tractor. There is a Happy Farmer distributor in your locality who will be glad to let you know when the next demonstration is to be held. Write us today for his name.

LA CROSSE TRACTOR COMPANY
Department 8259   La Crosse, Wisconsin

$1075

Farmers eager to learn

Farmers have flocked to machinery trials and demonstrations for more than 100 years. The diversity of tractors offered an excellent opportunity to stage such events. The steamers and big gas tractors had their day at the Winnipeg trials which were begun in 1908 and continued for many years. In the United States trials blossomed in many places. Perhaps the biggest was held at Champaign, Illinois, in August, 1915, sponsored by the University of Illinois, *Prairie Farmer* magazine, and other agricultural groups.

The most enduring of the tests was set up in Nebraska in 1920 under the auspices of the State of Nebraska and the University of Nebraska, assisted by the American Society of Agricultural Engineers and Society of Automotive Engineers. This was an effort to help farmers choose intelligently among literally scores of tractors of all sizes and shapes that had come on the market during and soon after World War I. The Nebraska trials attempted a scientific approach, measuring fuel consumption, drawbar and belt horsepower, and other features. Thus the Nebraska tests were an official yardstick for many years. In fact, there was a Nebraska Tractor Law which restricted the sale in that state of tractors that did not meet certain standards.

For most areas of the United States and Canada, however, the weeding out of ill-fitting and inferior tractor lines was done ruthlessly by the law of supply and demand after farmers had done their own testing. Wherever two

93

or three farmers got together, tractors were cussed and discussed and bragged about, much as the same farmers had discussed horses and mules in earlier days.

The spurt of mechanization on American farms which came with the introduction of the small gas tractor was of course only one chapter in the story of the farmer's love affair with invention and machinery. It began as early as the years of the Civil War and has continued to this day. The invention of the reaper and the saga of the steam threshing rig, which kept pace with the opening of the American West, are other exciting chapters.

The author's second book in this series, *Farm Inventions in the Making of America*, pays tribute to the country blacksmiths who originated many of the inventions that increased the productivity of our farms. The story of the small farm tractor, along with that of the farmer's flivver, is no less exciting and no less human.

JOHN DEERE took its time about getting seriously into the tractor business. Nevertheless its tractor line is one of the oldest, tracing its origins to the Froelich engine of 1892, which developed into the Waterloo Boy, manufactured for many years by the Waterloo Gas Engine Company of Waterloo, Iowa. The Waterloo advertisement is from 1918, the year John Deere absorbed the Waterloo line and received in the deal the durable two-cylinder engine that served for so many years. This is the engine with the "tut-tut" firing order that made it distinctive among farm tractors. On this page are two bread-and-butter John Deere tractors of the 1920s, a 15-27 with conventional four wheels and a row-crop which was Deere's contribution to the parade of tricycle types used so extensively in the 1920s and 1930s. Both tractors used the famous two-cylinder engine, in varying sizes.

It's More than a Success— It's a Real Sensation

That's the verdict coming from all over the country, wherever the John Deere Tractor is at work. Users get enthusiastic over its performance; neighbors join in—there's a real welcome for the

John Deere Tractor

HERE ARE THE REASONS:

Abundance of power to do all belt and drawbar work easily, rapidly and profitably.

Simpler by hundreds of parts, lighter by hundreds of pounds—a 15-27 tractor that weighs only 4,000 pounds—it does not pack the soil or mire down. Low and compact, it turns short and operates easily in close quarters.

Fewer and sturdier parts— made over-size—of the finest materials and workmanship.

Complete enclosure of working parts in a dust-proof, oil-tight case, thoroughly lubricated by a simple, positive oiling system.

Most efficient final drive ever designed for tractors. Double-roller chain of hardened steel, completely enclosed and running in oil bath. Ideal for saving power, and outlasts this long-lived tractor.

All adjustments and repairs can be made easily and quickly by the operator, in a standing position.

Low initial cost, fuel and oil economy, faster working speeds, low upkeep cost and long life make it a safe, money-making investment for the farmer.

The Improved John Deere
Shown with Inset Rear Wheels

—providing 68-inch tread for Potatoes and Other Narrow-Row Crops

The John Deere General Purpose Wide-Tread is a real cost-reducer in the growing of potatoes and other narrow-row crops. When used in these crops, the tractor is equipped with special inset rear wheels as shown at the left.

Equipped with a John Deere GP-240 Series Two-Row Cultivator, the tractor will cultivate from 15 up to 25 acres in a 10-hour day, doing better work than can be done with horses. Operating costs are lower than with other tractors because of the ability of this tractor to burn low-cost fuel.

95

J. I. CASE Threshing Machine Company, which had attained and held first place in the steam engine field, made an early start in gas engine experimentation and fielded a line of tractors almost from the beginning of the 1900s. The company seems to have avoided the really big engines, possibly to reduce competition with its well developed steam line. Shown here is the old 20-40 which was marketed in the 1912-16 years. This happens to be the model which the author cut his teeth on. By 1918 Case was building smaller tractors, including the three-wheeler which was abandoned after a few years. It then went back to a four wheel line in different ratings of horsepower, adding a row-crop when it became popular.

96

Keep The Boy In School

THE pressure of urgent spring work is often the cause of keeping the boy out of school for several months. It may seem necessary—but it isn't fair to the boy! You are placing a life handicap in his path if you deprive him of education. In this age, education is becoming more and more essential to success and prestige in all walks of life, including farming.

Should you feel that your own education was neglected, through no fault of yours, then you naturally will want *your* children to enjoy the benefits of a *real education*—to have some things you may have missed.

With the help of a Case Kerosene Tractor it is possible for one man to do more work, in a given time, than a good man and an industrious boy, together, working with horses. By investing in a Case Tractor and Grand Detour Plow and Harrow outfit *now*, your boy can get his schooling without interruption, and the Spring work will not suffer by his absence.

Keep the boy in school—and let a Case Kerosene Tractor take his place in the field. You'll never regret either investment.

J. I. Case Threshing Machine Company
Dept. C 26   Racine,   Wisconsin

CASE
TRADE MARKS REG. U.S. PAT. OFF.   AND IN FOREIGN COUNTRIES
KEROSENE TRACTORS

"NOTICE; We want the public to know that our plows and harrows are not the Case plows and harrows made by the J. I. Case Plow Works Co."

97

Boy mechanic is born

The human aspects of tractor mechanization deserve some attention in this volume, along with the story of manufacturing and development. This was the age of the boy mechanic, for it was the younger generation of farmers who embraced "tractorization" and who were most willing to give up horsemanship for the mechanization. The author was a farm boy during this period and savored the excitement of having a tractor to monkey with and to nurse through its moods and tantrums, which were numerous and varied. The two tractors that arrived on our home farm during this period were second hand and considerably the worse for wear. Father was an ardent horseman and was more likely to pick up an old tractor at a farm auction or in a horse trade than to walk into a dealer-

ADVERTISEMENTS on these two pages are from the year 1918. Note the wide range of Avery tractors in that year, from 5-10 to 40-80, with a special "motor cultivator" thrown in for good measure. Avery was one of the older companies that built its reputation first on steam and then on big gas tractors. When the small machines threatened to take over the market, even Avery had to respond with new designs and smaller horsepower.

Titan 12-25

Titan 18-35

Mogul 30-60

ship and buy a new one. That is exactly what happened.

Our first tractor was a 20-40 Case, two cylinders opposed, built on the scale of a steam engine. Father and my uncle who was a blacksmith-handyman needed an engine for belt work such as filling silo, grinding feed, and shredding corn (grain threshing still belonged to the itinerant steam rig). The eight horsepower single cylinder stationary with its massive flywheels and thunderous exhaust no longer filled the bill. Furthermore, it had driven everyone crazy by refusing to start. It took four stout horses to snake it on skids from one farm to another.

The ponderous Case was almost as stubborn, but at least it could travel under its own power. It ran on gasoline and used large quantities of heavy grade oil to lubricate the big cylinders. It was started with a crowbar inserted in a ratchet device on one end of the crankshaft. Two men could not pull the piston over the compression point, so compression was reduced by opening the priming petcocks which were first primed with liberal amounts of raw gasoline. Spark was furnished by a magneto. Each cylinder had two sparkplugs of the type which has changed very little down to the present.

When, after much grunting and groaning on the part of the operators, a cylinder fired with a great whoosh (petcock open) we hurried to close the cocks to get compression back to normal. Starting in cold weather was well-nigh impossible and presented a great challenge in corn shredding season which was usually midwinter. In desperation we would occasionally build a bonfire right under the engine to warm it. How we avoided destroying the tractor by fire can only be attributed to Providence and the zero Minnesota cold

100

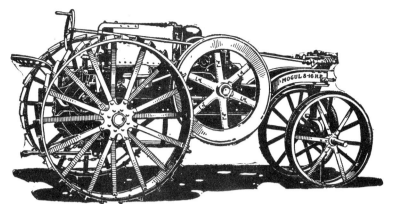

Mogul 8-16. $725 Cash f. o. b. Chicago

Titan
10-20

THE NAMES *Mogul* and *Titan* dominate the history of International Harvester tractors from the beginning until around 1920. The older models on the opposite page range from the experimental tractor at top, 1906, to two Moguls and two Titans from the years 1914 and 1915. By 1918 the Mogul and Titan lines had blossomed into a pair of relatively small farm tractors that established themselves solidly during the World War I years and for a time after. In the 1920s came the four-cylinder McCormick-Deering and the Farmall which was one of the first successful row-crop tractors. It is not widely known that before the Farmall came a motor cultivator model that bridged a gap to the conventional row-crop.

101

$^\$495$
F. O. B. Detroit
Fenders
$35 Extra

What a Difference the Fordson Makes!

When the weather is hot and the grain fast ripening, then Fordson owners fully appreciate the value of tractor power.

Many more acres harvested in a day than was possible in the old way—a big saving in hired help, in time, and in effort.

Belted to a separator, Fordson power makes threshing much easier. No delays—the whole job cleanly done and the grain ready for market.

Every farm task is performed with dispatch when the Fordson is put to work. Its cost is forgotten in the face of its splendid, satisfying performance.

Let the nearest authorized Ford dealer give you a practical demonstration of Fordson on your own land.

Ford Motor Company
Detroit, Michigan

Fordson

Getting the grain in quickly is as important as cutting it.

Ford trucks haul the bushels to market.

which greatly interfered with the ignition point of gasoline.

It was common in those days to have a gallon tin can handy filled with a mixture of gasoline and kerosene. A corncob on a rod was soaked in the mixture, ignited with a match and then applied to parts of the engine that needed warming, especially the manifold and the cylinders.

This Case had as radiator, a quadrangle of heavy finned pipes, which with the engine jacket held around 25 gallons of water. Movement of air through the radiator was accomplished by a stack which carried off the exhaust gases. There was no other provision for circulating either water or air. Antifreeze was out of the question in such a system, so the engine had to be drained every night in freezing weather.

This engine was mounted on a frame and wheels which had all the massiveness of steam gear. It handled like a stoneboat filled with rocks. In spite of all these frustrations we managed to get a lot of work out of the old 20-40, grading township roads, plowing, and a variety of belt work.

The second tractor to arrive on our farm was one of the earliest Fordsons, accompanied by a two-bottom plow. Father had bought it cheap at an auction. Since it was in bad shape, he instructed me, then a high school boy, to overhaul it from stem to stern. This was like overhauling a Model T, but on a larger scale. You took off the engine head, cleaned out the crud, and ground the valves. Then you took off the pan and set about tightening the connecting rods and main bearings. If the engine had been overhauled before, which was likely, there were no shims left to remove. So you got out a big flat file and filed down the bearing caps until you had a reasonably good fit. Then

you put the whole thing together again, trying not to have any parts left over.

The ignition on this Fordson, including the primitive timer and the spark coils, was so much like that of a Model T that it presented few problems for a boy mechanic.

Any farm boy who was anybody knew how to take a Model T apart on a weekend and put it together again. The Fordson was the same, only bigger. When I had overhauled the old clunker, it ran, much to my surprise, only not very well. When we boys went off to school, father sold the Fordson to a neighbor who was more of a tinkerer than a farmer, and went back to farming with horses.

Of course not all mechanics of that time were boys, but the younger generation of farmers have always had a special interest in mechanization of the American farm. Many years later (1960s), as editor of the Prairie Farmer I received an invitation from the American Society of Agricultural Engineers to speak at their regional meeting in Chicago. Casting about for a topic that would be helpful to designers and manufacturers of farm machinery, I bethought myself of the part played

THE FORDSON tractor hit farming like an explosion when it was unveiled in 1917, with all the productive power of the Ford Motor Company behind it. The year 1915 is usually considered its date of origin. Ford always took his time in getting tooled up for a successful run. He almost missed the lush war years, but his assembly line methods and wide dealership organization quickly pushed the Fordson right to the top in number of machines sold. The speed of the tractor in middle and high gear filled farmers with awe. Below is the first Fordson, about as simple a tractor as the Model T was a simple car. It had the same box of spark coils, the same timer, and much the same ignition system throughout. It burned kerosene after a gasoline start. The bare bones Fordson proved to be rather dangerous with its flashing lugs and tendency to rear up under a heavy load. The kick of the motor could also break your arm while you were cranking it. The advertisement on the opposite page a few years later reveals a changed hitch and fenders to cover the lugs, but it was essentially the same tractor, and remained the same for another 20 years.

by farm boys, and dispatched a questionnaire to members of the Future Farmers of America attending high schools all over the Middle West. I asked them to list both good and bad features of tractors being used on their home farms, and solicited their suggestions for improvement of machines in the future. It was a very informal and not very scientific bit of research, but the engineers ate it up and published the speech in their scholarly journal. The predictions of the boys as to what they wanted to happen bore a very close resemblance to what did actually happen in tractor design in later years.

104

RUMLEY was one of those well established steam threshing companies that shifted to large internal combustion tractors around 1910 to defend their market for big rigs in the Dakotas and Canada. Their Oil Pull tractors, almost from the first, had excellent engineering, having such features as oil cooling, kerosene fuel consumption, and water injection. Incorporating water injection as a function of carburetion is being talked of today. The designers of the big brutes of long ago knew that feeding water with the fuel made the engine knock less and run cooler. On this page is shown a 1912 tractor with two-cylinder horizontal engine set on a slant, which was believed to improve its performance. The advertisement on this page is also from 1912. The opposite page has a 1918 advertisement announcing one of Rumley's rather rare experiments in a smaller tractor designed to replace horses.

"It's just like handling a horse gang"

NOTICE the way the plows are hung on this Advance-Rumely "8-16"—right under and in front of you where you can see what's going on every minute—just the same as if you were sitting on a horse gang.

The "8-16" is a real one-man outfit—tractor and plows are combined in one machine and full control is from the driver's seat. With the "8-16" you can back up with your plows, make short turns and cut square corners.

Kerosene for Fuel

The Advance-Rumely "8-16" burns kerosene in such a way that it *pays* to burn it—not just under ideal conditions, but continuously and at variable loads.

The powerful, four-cylinder, heavy duty motor is Advance-Rumely built throughout.

For Drawbar or Belt

Besides being an efficient and easily handled outfit for plowing, discing, seeding, hauling and other drawbar jobs, the Advance-Rumely "8-16" is as efficient and economical on the belt—for threshing, baling, silo filling, husking, etc.

Detachable Plows

When used for jobs other than plowing you simply detach the plows and plow frame complete—a minute's work only.

A New Small Thresher

You can now get the famous "save-all-the-grain" Rumely Ideal Separator in a still smaller size—the 20x36 Junior Ideal. It is made to be run with a small tractor and is a *real* thresher—designed and built just like the larger Ideals.

Get These Catalogs

We have special catalogs on the Advance-Rumely "8-16" tractor and the new Ideal Junior separator. Just ask our nearest branch office.

ADVANCE-RUMELY THRESHER CO.

LAPORTE   (*Incorporated*)   INDIANA

Battle Creek, Mich.   Des Moines, Iowa
Indianapolis, Ind.   Madison, Wisc.
Peoria, Ill.

ADVANCE-RUMELY

1912—"Bear"

1914—"Model J"

1913—"Cub"

1919—Motor Cultivator

THE MASSEY-HARRIS line of tractors is one of the very oldest, going back to 1902 when the Racine, Wisconsin, firm built the Wallis Bear, one of the first four-cylinder machines. On this page is illustrated a succession of these tractors: the Big Bear as it looked in 1912, followed by 1913, 1914, and 1919 models. From this assortment it can be seen that Massey-Harris turned to smaller tractors at an early date, exploring thoroughly the three-wheelers in search of a good general farm tractor. At the bottom of the page are a conventional four-wheel Wallis of 1923 and the sensational, all-purpose, four wheel drive Massey-Harris of 1930.

180 companies in 1921

This book has traced so far the history of the gas tractor up to around 1920, with stress on the transition from the large tractor to the small, and the explosion of interest and inventiveness that occurred during World War I years when farm prices were good and the world was crying for more production. Tractor manufacturers reached a peak in number in 1921 with 186 firms in the business. The severe agricultural depression which began that same year dealt a stunning blow to the many small companies that had gotten into operation during the lush times. Larger firms tightened their belts and rode out the storm. Consolidations reduced the number of firms and the proliferation of models.

Undoubtedly the greatest development of the 1920s was the launching of the tricycle type row-crop tractor. International's Farmall started the trend in 1924 and before long virtually all the big manufacturers had one or more row-crops. The Cornbelt had come into its own. Acreages were being

shifted from small grains to corn. The farmer needed power to fight the weeds that were the enemies of this important crop. The weed chemicals had not yet arrived on the scene.

The row-crop tractors were uniformly small to medium in size, 10-20s and 15-30s being the most popular. They pulled two to three plow bottoms and were able to handle most farm operations quite well. They lent themselves well to tillage attachments that were attached directly to the tractor, even though hydraulic lifts and controls were still in the offing. Power takeoffs made it possible to dispense with the pulley and the belt, although the pulley lingered for some years as a necessary part of the tractor.

Farmers found these tractors somewhat lacking in power for the basic job of threshing, and some stuck with the itinerant steam rig and the threshing ring all through the 1920s. But most of them changed over to the small separators that were built by the leading manufacturers to fit small tractor power. The big 12-team threshing rings gave way to smaller groups of two or three farmers getting together to thresh more slowly with separators of modest size.

Housewives heaved sighs of relief upon being released from the necessity of feeding big crews at threshing time. To small boys, however, the passing of the big steam rig and its attendant threshing ring was something of a tragedy. The romance was gone — but not entirely! There was more demand for the work of boys in the smaller operations. Machinery was always exciting. Now when more farmers owned their own separators and used their own tractors there was more work than ever for the boy mechanic.

ANOTHER VERY OLD line of tractors was the Kinnard-Haines Flour City. This company launched a gas tractor line in 1897 by putting a single cylinder engine on a steam engine running gear. By the turn of the century this effort had grown into the ponderous Flour City line which was quite prominent in the first decade of the 1900s wherever big tractors were used. The year 1916 saw the first attempt at a smaller tractor, shown in the advertisement at the right. The big 40-70 at the bottom of the page shows what the company's line of big tractors looked like in 1920. Based in Minneapolis, this is one of the companies that had a stake in the threshing and plowing activities of the Dakotas which called for big horsepower.

-The most efficient tractor in America-

The JOHNSON TRACKPULL

Clutch Controlled and Steered

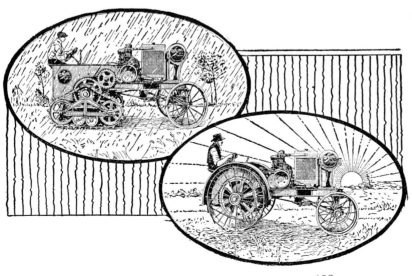

Big tractors in comeback

The big tractor did not disappear during the 1920s. The day of the steamer was definitely past, but the consolidation of farms was beginning. Most companies extended and improved their tractor lines across the full spectrum of power requirements. Bankruptcies and consolidations steadily reduced the number of firms in the business. The larger farms of the Great Plains wheat belt and parts of the South and West needed big tractors and bought them in considerable numbers in spite of the fact that agriculture remained in economic doldrums all through the 1920s and on through the even worse 1930s.

This volume is essentially a history and will not undertake to trace the development of the tractor after 1930, which year was a kind of watershed in the history of mechanization. From that date horses were definitely out of the running. Small and large tractors were being put on rubber. Tractor engines followed the lead of automobiles that featured higher compression and used high octane fuel. The diesel, although invented in the early years of the internal combustion era, was slow to reach the farm, but it was on the way. In the meantime even the large tractors abandoned kerosene and cruder distillates and went to gasoline. Governments which discovered the gas tax as a relatively painless source of revenue were careful to avoid taxing agricultural fuel.

The self-propelled machine such as the combine and the picker-sheller was in the making, as was the power unit that could take on many agricultural attachments and thereby use the same engine for many purposes. Tires got bigger and bigger, duals became common, and four-wheel drive systems were invented to improve traction. Crawler tractors enjoyed a good deal of popularity during the transition period, but they too began to give way to big pneumatic tires.

The years since 1930 have not lacked excitement in the mechanization field. However, the small manufacturers and inventors have passed from the scene. Only the big ones can hack it now. Engineering has moved out of the farm shop into the industrial laboratory. The farm youth, proudly maneuvering his big diesel around the larger family farm, is still an advocate of mechanization. But he knows less about the inner workings of the tractor he controls so adroitly. He will hesitate to get out his wrenches and take the thing apart, as his father did when he was a boy. Something has been lost which we boys of the 1910-1930 years treasured. We learned a lot during those years when we were putting farming on wheels.

ENGINEERS WORKED HARD at putting the small tractor on tracks to achieve the kind of traction needed for light weight machines, as illustrations on these two pages will testify. Bates Steel Mule had an alternate set of tracks in 1918. The same was true of the Acme tractor (lower left-hand page) about the same time. Belle City of Racine marketed a set of tracks for the Fordson in 1923. Just below is the small high-clearance cat marketed by Caterpillar (formerly Holt) in 1931. Cletrac by Cleveland was a popular small crawler from 1919 on through the 20s. From 1935 on rubber tires killed the interest in the small crawlers.

$595

F. O. B.
Upper
Sandusky,
Ohio

AMONG THE 180 tractor makes manufactured around 1920 are names unheard of today, except perhaps by a few tractor buffs who know their history. The Whitney (1921) and the Sandusky (1915) are relatively unknown. The Samson (1918) set out to steal the show from Fordson but did not succeed. The GO reveals a manufacturer of World War I ordnance trying to break into the crowded tractor field.

SAMSON (Model M)
Complete with power take-off and automatic control
$650.00 f o. b. Janesville, Wis.

The General Ordnance Company

General Offices:
TWO WEST 43rd STREET, NEW YORK

Western Sales Office and Works:
CEDAR RAPIDS, IA.

THE G O COMPANY OF TEXAS
Dallas, Texas

Eastern Works:
DERBY, CONNECTICUT

110

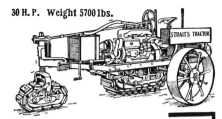
HERE ARE some unusual tractors that have faded from the scene. The Strait (1916) had a most unorthodox traction arrangement. The Huber (1918) bore a venerable name from the steam era. Whoever heard of the Boring (1921) manufactured at Rockford, Illinois?

"Give us a tractor that is not only profitable for threshing but of general use on the farm," they said.   We responded with the

HUBER
Super Four Tractor

You have no idea how well the Huber Super Four measures up to the demand for general usefulness, unless you own one or have seen the tractor at work.

It is a high-powered machine.   It must be or it would not do for profitable threshing. But the ability to muster great power doesn't prevent the Huber Super Four from being entirely suitable and useful for plowing and general farm work. Lightness has been secured through simplified design and correct weight distribution.

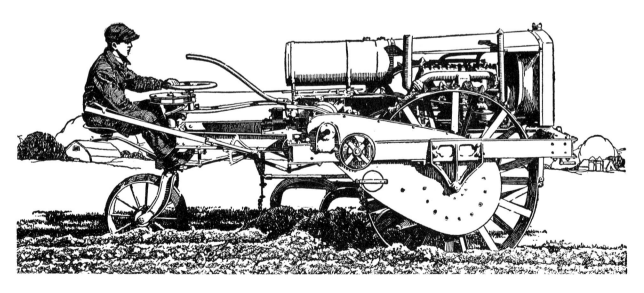

MINNEAPOLIS Threshing Machine Company once had a line of steam engines and separators among the best known in the Great Plains wheat country. Top illustration is one of their big 35-70 gas tractors which, along with the Twin City line, was absorbed into Minneapolis-Moline.

Twin City
17-28 Tractor

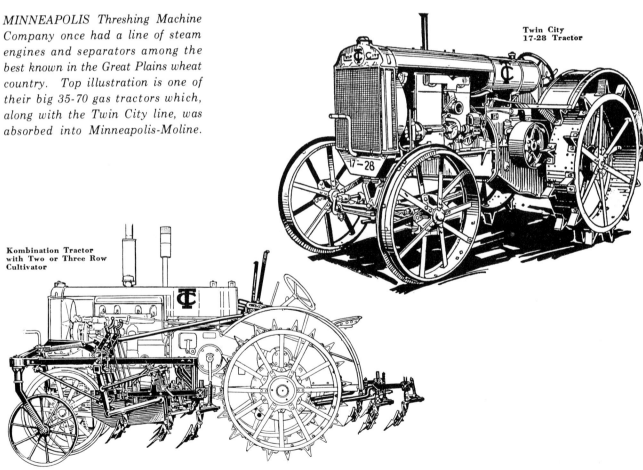

Kombination Tractor
with Two or Three Row
Cultivator

HERE ARE *three obscure tractors from the year 1918. Top illustration, the Stinson made in Minneapolis; center, the Parrett made in Chicago; bottom, the Nilson made in Minneapolis. Minnesota's Twin Cities were big in the tractor field.*

18-36

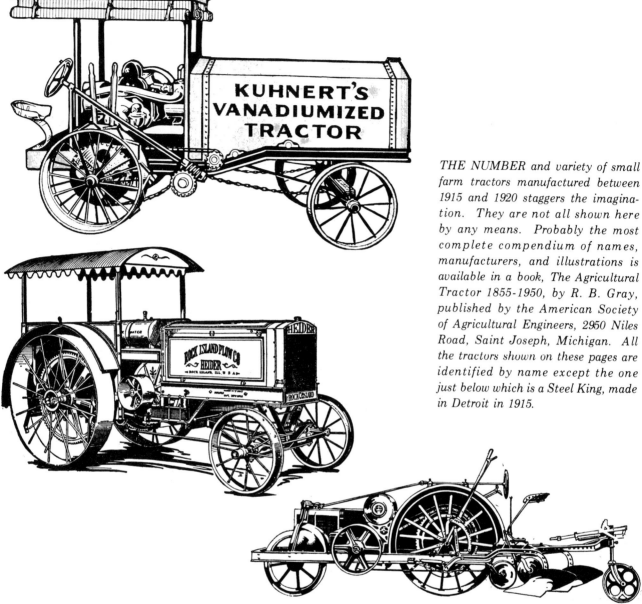

KUHNERT'S VANADIUMIZED TRACTOR

THE NUMBER and variety of small farm tractors manufactured between 1915 and 1920 staggers the imagination. They are not all shown here by any means. Probably the most complete compendium of names, manufacturers, and illustrations is available in a book, The Agricultural Tractor 1855-1950, by R. B. Gray, published by the American Society of Agricultural Engineers, 2950 Niles Road, Saint Joseph, Michigan. All the tractors shown on these pages are identified by name except the one just below which is a Steel King, made in Detroit in 1915.

114

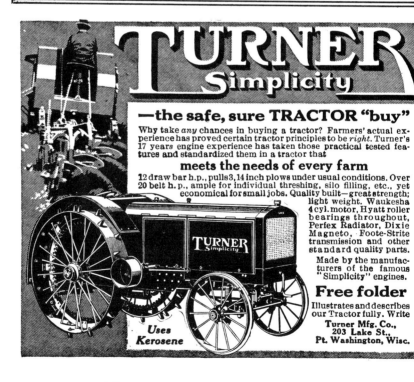

1,278,217.

Patented Sept. 10, 1918.

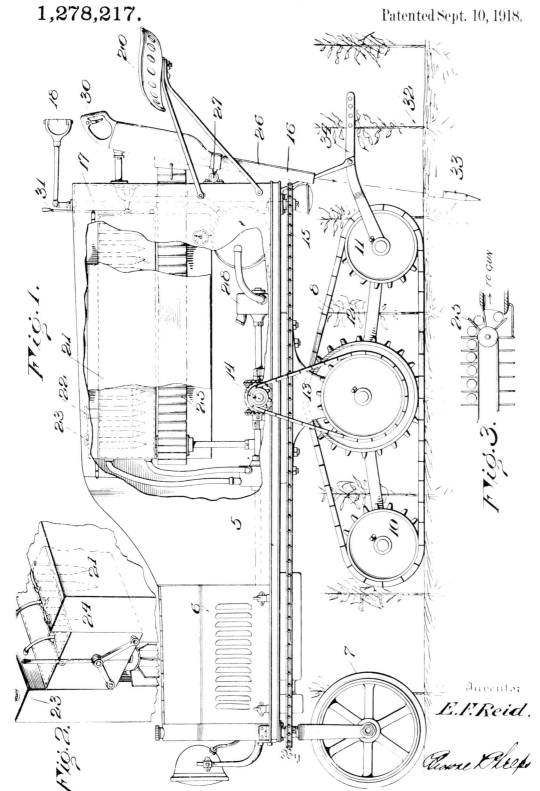

Fig. 1.

Fig. 2.

Fig. 3.

Inventor
E. F. Reid.

116

ALL THE TRACTORS *illustrated in this volume were actually built and put on the market, with more or less success. At the same time hundreds of "screwball" patents having to do with adaptations of the gas tractor to agriculture were run through the U. S. Patent Office in Washington. No compendium of tractor information would be complete without at least a quick glance at this aspect of tractor lore. Herewith are presented a plant irrigator and a grasshopper harvester. Needless to say, the period covered in this book represents a rich lode of patent ideas. Tribute should be paid to the thousands of inventors who hoped to get rich with their mechanical schemes. As with other farm machinery, most of the progress during this period had its roots in ideas worked up by farm handymen and back alley inventors. Some of their patents were sold to established manufacturers. Others were actually put into tangible form by the inventor who became a manufacturer, only to have to sell out to the big guys. After 1930 development moved into the big industrial laboratories, aided by the agricultural engineering departments of land-grant universities.*

W. D. KEMP.
GRASSHOPPER HARVESTER.
APPLICATION FILED JAN. 9, 1919.

1,325,475.

Patented Dec. 16, 1919.
3 SHEETS—SHEET 2.

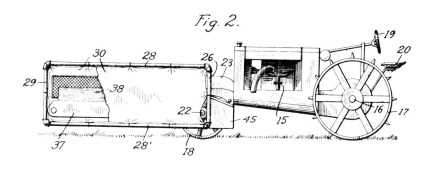

Fig. 2.

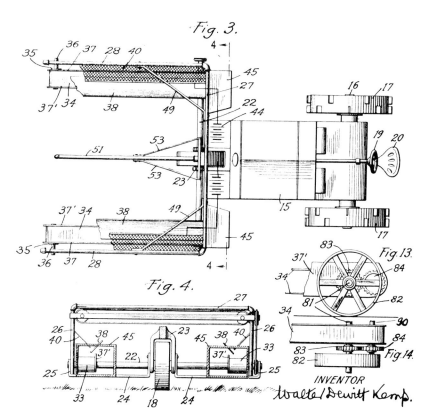

Fig. 3.

Fig. 13.

Fig. 4.

Fig. 14.

INVENTOR
Walter Dewitt Kemp.

117

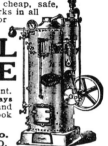

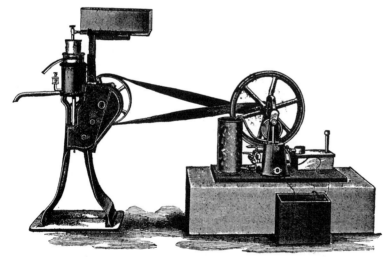

FARMSTEAD
Small engines and electricity

From pioneer days down to recent times the farmer's wife has been compelled to wait for her laborsaving appliances until the farm and barn have been properly mechanized. Only in the last generation has the household received equal billing with the rest of the farm in modernization. Small engines were built in the latter part of the 1800s to help out with farmstead chores, but they did not give much comfort to the homemaker.

Engines were used for pumping water, operating butter churns and cream separators, running washing machines, all of which were considered women's work. However, women did not take readily to wrestling with balky engines. There was scant comfort in having household machines hooked up to power if your washing and churning could only be done when there were men around to start the engines and keep them running. So a lot of these jobs were done by hand long after the engines were invented.

Nevertheless, much of the advertising by manufacturers was directed at keeping the housewife happy. In 1904 a Fairbanks-Morse advertisement in *Indiana Farmer's Guide* trumpeted:

"If you love your wife, buy a Fairbanks-Morse engine for churning, pumping, grinding, and separating cream. Simple, safe, economical, reliable. Guaranteed."

Such a statement may have fitted the electric motors that came to the farm in a later day,

but they did not accurately describe what you let women in for when it came to handling the first gas engines. It was not until around 1915, when Maytag came out with a small built-in washing machine engine which you could start with a kick of your foot, that women began to feel at home with engines. The Briggs and Stratton era when little engines could be kicked or jerked into quick action was still some decades off.

For the menfolk the little engines were a boon, well worth the trouble it took to coax them into action. It took a lot of muscle to crank a Fuller and Johnson pump engine. Most engines did not have a crank and had to be started by manhandling the flywheels. Carburetion was primitive, consisting often of a simple vacuum-operated intake valve sucking the gas right out of the gas tank. Ignition was by dry cell batteries which had a way of wearing out rapidly. Primitive igniters were used instead of spark plugs. In extremely cold weather batteries had to be hauled in the house and warmed by the stove or they wouldn't function at all. Cylinder lubrication was achieved by a very simple drip system that fed the oil by gravity from a small vial.

All these things added up to a lot of trouble and uncertainty. Women often preferred to go back to the old hand crank.

Some of the engines were made around the turn of the century by tractor manufacturers, but quite a number of small firms got into

Fits Any Pump and Makes It Hump!

Patented in the United States, Canada and other foreign countries. Other patents applied for.

Works As If It Owned The Farm

There isn't any loafing when you turn a job over to the

Fairbanks-Morse *Eclipse Engine*

Makes a specialty of pumping water day in and day out all the year round.

Every pump should have an *Eclipse Engine.*

It's a high grade, labor saving engine made in No. 1 and No. 2 sizes.

Prices are low, quality considered and the engines are ready to ship.

Do you want catalog No. JE 1070

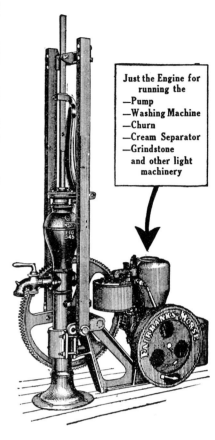

Just the Engine for running the
—Pump
—Washing Machine
—Churn
—Cream Separator
—Grindstone
and other light machinery

Fairbanks, Morse & Co.

Manufacturers of Oil Engines, Pumps, Windmills and other machinery.

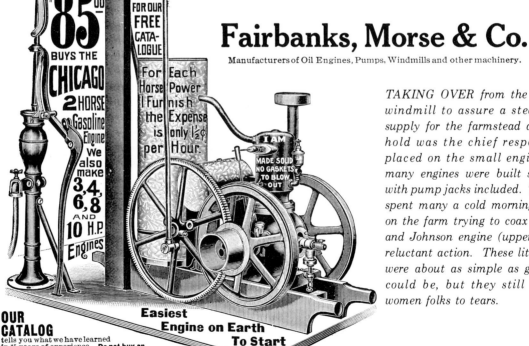

$85.00 BUYS THE CHICAGO 2 HORSE Gasoline Engine We also make 3,4, 6,8 AND 10 H.P. Engines

WRITE FOR OUR FREE CATALOGUE

For Each Horse Power I Furnish the Expense is only 1½¢ per Hour

Easiest Engine on Earth To Start

OUR CATALOG tells you what we have learned in 15 years of experience. Do not buy an engine of any kind, a wind mill or any kind of power until you receive our handsome catalog and learned all about our engine and see our low prices.

CHICAGO GASOLINE ENGINE CO.

TAKING OVER from the unreliable windmill to assure a steady water supply for the farmstead and household was the chief responsibility placed on the small engine; hence many engines were built specifically with pump jacks included. The author spent many a cold morning as a boy on the farm trying to coax the Fuller and Johnson engine (upper left) into reluctant action. These little engines were about as simple as gas engines could be, but they still drove the women folks to tears.

120

the business. It seems that a great many of them sprang up in Iowa, Cedar Rapids, Des Moines, and Waterloo. Waterloo was undoubtedly the capital of the small engine business. At one time there must have been about a dozen manufacturers operating out of there.

Stationary, single-cylinder gas engines ranged in size from one and a half horsepower up to eight horsepower or more. In the larger sizes they were pressed into service to grind feed, saw wood, fill silo, gin cotton, press sorghum, bale hay and handle some heavy farmstead jobs. Some, as has been noted in an earlier chapter, sprouted wheels of their own and became tractors.

When the big tractors gave way to smaller, more versatile machines, these took over the intermediate farmstead tasks and the big stationaries faded from the scene entirely. However, small power plants for household tasks were still a necessity.

The electric motor finally came to the rescue of the beleaguered housewife, after much travail on the part of practically everyone. Most farmers did not have access to power lines from central generators, except at horrendous cost, say $1000 per mile for running new lines. It took until the 1930s for farmers to secure government help to build their own lines and dicker

with the power companies for "juice" at wholesale rates.

Before this happened was invented the small electric light plant, a gas or kerosene burning engine hooked to a small generator that charged 16 big glass battery cells generating 32 volts. Farm homes were wired, and wiring was also extended frugally to outbuildings. The main purpose of this was to obtain the electric light that transformed rural life. Well charged batteries produced rather good light in 25 watt bulbs, but as batteries ran down or deteriorated with age, the engine-generator had to be run more and more. Lights tended to go dim between runs.

Electric motors were something of a lost cause. One or two quarter-horse motors constituted a full load. The highest priority for motor use went for pumping water. Separating cream, churning but-

ter and washing clothes had a lower priority. Refrigerators were still run with a primitive kerosene burning unit that avoided a compression pump. Milking machines, cooling fans, and electric food mixers edged their way into the power train.

There wasn't enough "umph" in the 32-volt plants to do very much in the way of furnishing farmstead power. Even so they were a godsend to the woman of the house who hated and feared gas engines.

Farmers that tired of their gasoline light plants and still stubbornly refused to come to terms with power companies and cooperatives had a try at generating their own electricity from the tops of old windmill towers. Thus was born the windcharger that is under close scrutiny today as a means of saving energy. The farmers back in the 1920s who first tried

THE WITTE advertisement at right has an inset diagram of the igniter that preceded the spark plug as the dispenser of spark for the engines of that day. Timing was not very precise but it worked fairly well — most of the time. The smallest engines had no cooling except fins, or they had a water jacket without circulation.

wind-produced electricity found out that it was not adequate to take care of the enormous power needs of the modern farm which now has come to take for granted at least 20 motors of various sizes, to say nothing of heating elements for a variety of purposes.

One of the first things wind-charger enthusiasts learn in our day is that a small generator can only be a standby arrangement unless a lot of our power hungry appliances are dispensed with.

Young homemakers now take abundant household power for granted. They have to ask their grandmothers about the day when there were only two options, a balky gas engine or a hand crank.

It is ironic that the greatest success with small gas engines came only after electricity on the farm was almost universal. Along about that time excellent small engines were designed, both two-cycle and four-cycle. Dozens of uses for portable power came out of nowhere, the power lawnmover, snowmobile, outboard motor, emergency generator, auxiliary motor for field machines, well pump away from the farmstead. Small engines are in wider use than ever. Fortunately they are better engineered and the old frustrations have been largely lifted.

LARGER stationary gas engines were put on wheels and used for farm belt work, even for threshing grain. Their horsepower was usually inadequate for heavy jobs, resulting in a rapid shift to bigger gas tractors after the turn of the century. Note that Olds of Lansing, Michigan, made gas engines and even turned out a few self-propelled tractors.

THIS REMARKABLE engraving from a 1891 issue of the American Agriculturist published in the East shows an attempt to thresh grain with a large electric motor. The practice did not catch on for several reasons. Most farmers were not situated on electric high lines. The small light plants that became quite common on farms from 1915 on did not have the voltage and wattage to handle such big jobs. However, the urge to use electric power on the farm was present even before 1900. Large electric motors were not feasible for farm power on a broad scale until rural electric co-operatives became common in the 1930s.

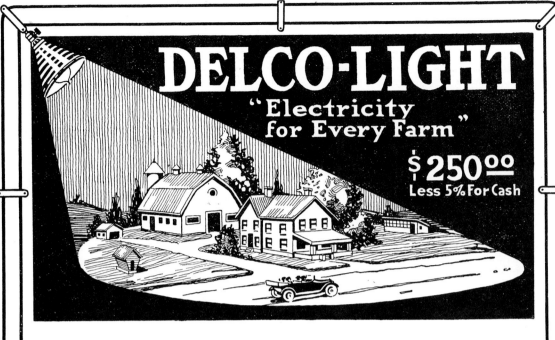

A FLOOD OF LIGHT

Delco Light brings city advantages to the farm. Furnishes electricity for both light and power—takes much of the drudgery out of farm work—adds comfort and convenience to farm life.

Gas Engine and Dynamo in one compact unit—so simple that a child can operate it. Nothing to get out of order or go wrong—starts itself and stops automatically when batteries are fully charged.

Furnishes 40 to 50 lights for house and barn and provides power for churn, cream separator, washing machine, sewing machine, etc.

Lights average home for less than 5 cents a day.

Complete with batteries, ready to run $250

Write for Illustrated Folder

Manufactured by the same Company that makes Delco Cranking, Lighting and Ignition for automobiles— That in itself is a guarantee of quality.

The Domestic Engineering Company, Dayton, Ohio

General Agents

Domestic Electric Co., 315 S. Jefferson St., Peoria, Ill.
E. L. Kruse, 60 W. New York St., - Indianapolis, Ind.
J. S. Kimmel, Hotel Davenport Bldg., Davenport, Iowa

AROUND THE YEAR 1915 electricity became a passion with farmers — even those who had no opportunity for high line service. The answer was a 32-volt plant with a gas or kerosene engine with built-in generator. The electric light was prized much more highly than the power, however. Heavy use of electric power on the farm came much later, around the year 1935 with the arrival of REA.

ALAMO Electricity

Power and Light On *Your* Farm

LIKE all modern agricultural equipment, electricity on the farm has come to stay. It is a work-reducing and comfort-giving necessity — an essential utility that plays an important part in the war work of the farm.

With ALAMO ELECTRICITY farmers now do several hours' extra work daily and do it easier. It lights the house, barn, out-buildings and yards like day. It aids men's work by grinding feed, pumping water, running milkers, cream separators and many other light machines.

Woman's Greatest Helper

The drudgery of woman's work can be eliminated by ALAMO ELECTRICITY. It runs her washing machine, wringer, churn, sewing machine, vacuum sweeper, and other labor saving devices. It heats her flat iron and makes ironing a pleasure. An electric fan makes kitchen work comfortable. Electric lights relieve strain.

Low Operating Cost

The ALAMO performs all these tasks at low cost and requires but little attention. Its sturdy construction assures lifetime wear. Its many exclusive features make it the perfected unit. It requires no special foundation — install it in the most convenient place and it will furnish ample power and light without vibration or noise.

A special engine was built for the Alamo — the Ide Super-Silent Motor. This power marvel has no springs, cams or rods to get out of adjustment. It clears itself of carbon. Its fuel-saving carburetor makes it a wonder for economy.

Send For Latest Electrical Farming Book

Send the coupon today for valuable information about electricity on the farm and details of the famous ALAMO UNIT. Get these facts whether you intend to buy now or not. Do it now.

ALAMO FARM LIGHT COMPANY

General Offices: 1233 Farnam St., Omaha, Neb.

Factories:
Hillsdale, Michigan

(25)

Alamo Farm Light Company,
1233 Farnam Street,
Omaha, Neb.

Plese send your ALAMO BOOK of farm light and power facts and information about the ALAMO UNIT.

Name ....

Postoffice.............. R. F. D.....

County............ State..........

"THE NATION KNOWS THE ALAMO"

126

AUTOMOBILES

Boosted power on farms

The automobile is not, strictly speaking, a source of power for farming. It is rather a means of transportation. However, cars and trucks are so closely associated with the power story that they deserve at least a brief mention in this volume.

The mechanization of transportation and of farm work were from almost the beginning cut from the same fabric. The engines were pretty much the same. The human input of mechanical ingenuity was the same. The development of the gas tractor received great impetus from the technology of the automobile.

What is more, there was an urge which we have almost lost sight of today to use the motor vehicle to do the farm work that we expected of the tractor. We sense just a touch of this same motivation in the four-wheel drive pickups and jeep types that are so widely used today.

The home mechanic developed at an early date an itch to turn his car into a tractor, to save money, to utilize outdated cars, or just for the heck of it. Even before 1920 there grew up a backyard science of putting traction wheels on old cars. Eager manufacturers, usually small operators who made a living by filling in gaps, got on the bandwagon and turned out "kits" that would change a car into a tractor or a serviceable truck. They did a considerable business for a time, although backyard mechanics mostly turned up their noses at such prefabricated stuff and set about designing their own conversions.

It has been said that the enterprising firms which designed and built gadgets and accessories for Henry Ford's Model T and Model A cars made more money than Ford himself. Ford cars were very much the object of these tractor conversion kits. Some firms did, however, try to make their conversions fit other cars than the Ford.

The Model T was the ordinary man's car during those years when small tractors were taking over farming. The price of a Ford roadster dropped as low as $350, thanks to the Ford assembly line and other shortcuts in production. To begin with there were only about two variations of the Model T, the roadster one-seater and the four-door touring car. It may be necessary here to remind younger generations that in early models the Ford had only three doors, conveniently omitting a door next to the driver. The other significant shortcut was that you could have any color you wanted just so it was black.

Most cars of the early 1900s were quite heavy. Farmers bought them freely because they were prosperous during those World War I years before the farm depression of 1921. Builders of big cars that went after the farm market by advertising in farm papers included Krit, Reo, Hupmobile, Buick, Studebaker, Overland, Chalmers, Mitchell, Hudson, Paige, Oldsmobile, Jeffrey — to mention the most common.

The first small car to challenge Ford was, not Chevrolet as you might have expected, but Maxwell. Chevrolet and Star came

Don't experiment - Just buy a FORD

THE UNKNOWN FORD — 1906

Ford Touring Car

EVERYBODY'S TIN LIZZIE — 1912-17

later, just after 1920.

The Ford Company spread into the truck field almost at once. The Model T wasn't any heavyweight, as you might expect, but it hauled a lot of farm produce just the same. The little Model T motor groaned and grunted under one ton loads, but it was tough. Its progress was slow, its motor at boiling point continually, and long hills were murder, but it seldom gave up. The International Harvester Company started putting out heavier duty trucks soon after the turn of the century and has stayed with the business down to the present time. Another heavier truck called the Masters went after farm business in the years just after the war. Maxwell and later Chevrolet moved into the light truck field with considerable success. Most farmers did not buy trucks, however. Instead they piled the back seat of the touring car full of practically every kind of farm produce, including livestock, and managed to get along without trucks.

Quite a few motor car companies tried to build a small tractor, but not many of the farm machinery firms tried their luck in the crowded auto field. J. I. Case took a flier at a farm car in 1915 but soon returned to the steam and gas tractor lines that Case dealers knew best how to handle.

Only a limited number of the scores of makes of automobiles that were put on the market before 1930 are illustrated here. Most of them were not notably successful. After 1920, as with the small tractors, cars failed in droves. Many did not even merit consolidation with more successful lines. The number of companies got fewer and fewer. When Ford abandoned the very versatile Model A and started to build V-8 engines in the early 1930s, it was a new ball game in the auto business as well as in the tractor field. Power in both farm work and transportation had taken over farming. The horse faded from the scene as a work animal. Petroleum products stayed relatively cheap for a half century longer.

The real crisis did not come until the 1970s when it became clear that there would have to be a reassessment of farm power sources along with all other power sources. Economists began asking, Are we pouring more energy into power farming than we are getting from the land in return? It may not be fair to equate the fossil fuels that power mechanized farming with the food for human beings that is the principal product of farming. But shortages are a serious matter. The current effort is to make petroleum engines more efficient. There is still much to be done along this line. But eventually there will have to be a shift to other sources of farm power. Will it be wind? Will it be steam generated by cheaper fuels? Will it be alcohol, permitting the internal combustion engine, like the horse before it, to eat the products of its own labor? Or will it be something entirely new?

FORD TRUCK — 1919

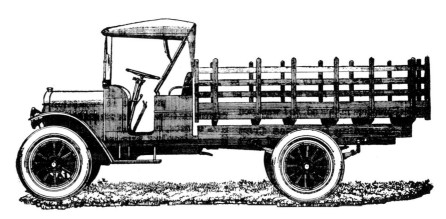

MAXWELL TRUCK — 1919

INTERNATIONAL TRUCK — 1919

129

Abbott:Detroit "30"
Fore-Door Roadster, $1275

DETROITER — 1912

Studebaker

The $800
Studebaker (Flanders) "20"

Equipped with Top, Windshield
Prest-O-Lite Tank and Speed-
ometer, $885 f. o. b. Detroit.

STUDEBAKER — 1912

Reo the Fifth

**1914
Summer
Series**

Completely Equipped
Electric Starter and Lights

Now $1,175

Touring Car
or Roadster

KRIT — 1912

J. I. CASE CAR — 1915

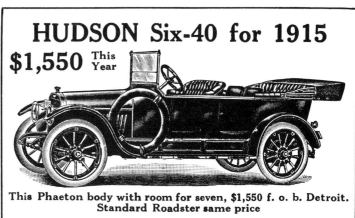

HUDSON Six-40 for 1915

$1,550 This Year

This Phaeton body with room for seven, $1,550 f. o. b. Detroit.
Standard Roadster same price

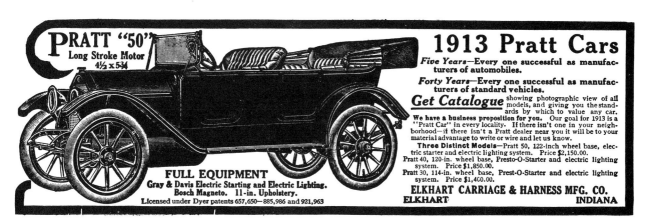

PRATT "50"
Long Stroke Motor
4½ x 5¾

1913 Pratt Cars

Five Years—Every one successful as manufacturers of automobiles.

Forty Years—Every one successful as manufacturers of standard vehicles.

Get Catalogue showing photographic view of all models, and giving you the standards by which to value any car.

We have a business proposition for you. Our goal for 1913 is a "Pratt Car" in every locality. If there isn't one in your neighborhood—if there isn't a Pratt dealer near you it will be to your material advantage to write or wire and let us know.

Three Distinct Models—Pratt 50, 122-inch wheel base, electric starter and electric lighting system. Price $2,150.00.
Pratt 40, 120-in. wheel base, Presto-O-Starter and electric lighting system. Price $1,850.00.
Pratt 30, 114-in. wheel base, Prest-O-Starter and electric lighting system. Price $1,400.00.

ELKHART CARRIAGE & HARNESS MFG. CO.
ELKHART   **INDIANA**

FULL EQUIPMENT
Gray & Davis Electric Starting and Electric Lighting.
Bosch Magneto. 11-in. Upholstery.
Licensed under Dyer patents 657,650—885,986 and 921,963

131

METZ — 1914

*Friction drive, no clutch,
no transmission*

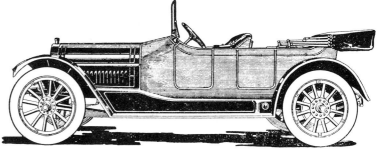

MITCHELL — 1912

MAXWELL — 1919

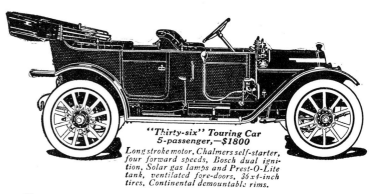

"Thirty-six" Touring Car
5-passenger,—$1800

*Long stroke motor, Chalmers self-starter,
four forward speeds, Bosch dual ignition, Solar gas lamps and Prest-O-Lite
tank, ventilated fore-doors, 36 x 4-inch
tires, Continental demountable rims.*

"Leans Right Up In the Collar and Pulls"

CHALMERS — 1912

PAIGE — 1919

CHEVROLET — 1921

OVERLAND — 1923

STAR — 1925

ESSEX — 1923

DODGE BROTHERS — 1923

Oakland "6"

The
1923 Oaklands

Roadster	$ 975
Sport Roadster	1145
Sport Touring	1165
Coupe for Two	1185
Coupe for Five	1445
Sedan	1545

Prices f. o. b. Factory

Bibliographical Comment

Bound volumes of old farm magazines, some going back to the 1850s, have been the principal source of illustrations and information for this volume. The material is from nearly a dozen such publications. However the chief sources have been three of the oldest, *Prairie Farmer, American Agriculturist,* and the *Cultivator-Country Gentlemen* succession. All are in existence today, although there is argument about the matter of uninterrupted publication. *Prairie Farmer* has been publishing under the same name since 1841.

Original magazine sources have a great advantage for the researcher in that the engravings from advertisements tell more about the components of each machine than is possible with photographs, most of which were rather poor in quality. Anyone interested in farm history might well latch onto any bound volume prior to 1920 which may appear in antique shows or auction sales. Of course, loose copies are just as good and more likely to turn up.

Another source available to the author is a fairly complete set of Department of Agriculture yearbooks from the 1850s, 60s, and 70s. Before the organization of the Department in 1862, the reports were issued by the U. S. Patent Office. These old volumes have excellent material on the development of agricultural steam engines in England and in the United States during those exciting years when steam was coming into its own. The early USDA source is the more valuable because of its close connection with the patent information which was kept just around the corner.

Around 1940 the yearbooks were given a single theme each year, making it easier to trace useful material. The 1960 yearbook entitled *Power to Produce* contains much helpful information on the history of power in farming.

Another revealing source of historical material is, of course, the advertising leaflets and brochures put out by the companies themselves. Some of these embraced color in their presentations before color became common in farm paper advertisements.

The celebration of centennials by publications and manufacturers, as well as the recent bicentennial, was occasion for publications containing much historical material. Special anniversary publications by magazines worth special mention are the *Prairie Farmer* issue of 1941, the *Country Gentleman* special issue of 1831, and the bicentennial edition of *The Furrow* put out by John Deere in 1976.

Anniversary books include the Caterpillar book, *"Fifty Years on Tracks,"* put out in 1954. A fascinating book and precious source of history is one commissioned by the J. I. Case Company on its centennial, *Machines of Plenty,* by Stewart H. Holbrook, the MacMillan Company, New York, 1955. There are of course others which may not have come to the attention of the author. International Harvester Company has issued much excellent material, as has John Deere in connection with its excellent museum at Moline, Illinois.

There are two scholarly, carefully researched books which should be in the hands of every steam and gas tractor buff who wants to dig deeper. One is *The Agricultural Tractor 1855-1950,* by R. B. Gray, American Society of Agricultural Engineers, 2950 Niles Road, Saint Joseph, Michigan, revised 1975. This has the most complete set of pictures ever compiled of tractors. It also has the best compendium of statistics of the tractor industry, as well as lists of manufacturers and consolidations.

Another scholarly book, concentrating on steam but also having good information on other machinery, is *Steam Power on the American Farm,* by Reynold M. Wik, University of Pennsylvania Press, Philadelphia, 1953.

For those interested in windmills must reading is *Windmills and Watermills,* by John Reynolds, Praeger Publishers, 111 Fourth Avenue, New York, N. Y., 1970. This has probably the most definitive treatment of these ancient and increasingly contemporary sources of power. It has photos and drawings showing details of construction not to be found anywhere else.

The sources mentioned here are only some of the most valuable among hundreds of references that might be compiled. They are mentioned so that the farm power enthusiast who is not a professional researcher can obtain them without too much trouble or expense.

Good hunting!

The author

Paul C. Johnson was for 22 years editor and editorial director of *Prairie Farmer*, an agricultural magazine which was founded in 1841 at Chicago and is still going strong. The nearly complete files of *Prairie Farmer* going back to the date of founding have been a rich source of agricultural history and inspiration. Reared on a Minnesota dairy farm, Johnson spent ten years as a country newspaper editor and seven years on the faculty of the Institute of Agriculture of the University of Minnesota before zeroing in on farm magazine editing and agricultural history. He is a past president of both the American Agricultural Editors Association and the American Country Life Association. He has won many awards in his field, including the honorary degree of Doctor of Humane Letters from St. Olaf College.

Johnson's keen interest in farm machinery goes back to his childhood on the farm. As one of the founders of the famous Farm Progress Show in the Middle West, sponsored annually by *Prairie Farmer, Wallaces Farmer,* and *Wisconsin Agriculturist,* known as the Farm Progress Publications, the author of this volume had a rare opportunity to work with modern machinery manufacturers as well as pursuing his hobby of studying their history.

After retiring in 1970, Johnson and his wife Eveline moved to the home community of Northfield, Minnesota, where they have been editing and writing books on agricultural history and antiques. Post-retirement books by Johnson include the following:

John Turnipseed's Four Seasons Almanac, softbound, Wallace-Homestead Book Co., 1973, $2.00.

Farm Animals in the Making of America, softbound, Wallace-Homestead Book Co., 1976, $4.95.

Farm Inventions in the Making of America, softbound, Wallace-Homestead Book Co., 1976, $4.95.

Farm Power in the Making of America, softbound, color, Wallace-Homestead Book Co., 1978, $6.95.

Any orders sent directly to the publisher for books should be accompanied by 50 cents (added to the basic book price) to cover the cost of shipping. The publisher's address is Wallace-Homestead Book Co., P.O. Box BI, Des Moines, Iowa 50304.